McGraw-Hill Ryerson

Principles of Mathematics 9

Student Skills Book

AUTHORS

Chris Dearling
B.Sc., M.Sc.
Burlington, Ontario

Wayne Erdman
B.Math, B.Ed.
Toronto District School Board

Fred Ferneyhough
B.Math.
Peel District School Board

Brian McCudden
M.A., M.Ed., Ph.D.
Toronto, Ontario

Fran McLaren
B.Sc., B.Ed.
Upper Grand District School Board

Roland W. Meisel
B.Sc., B.Ed., M.Sc.
Port Colborne, Ontario

Jacob Speijer
B.Eng., M.Sc.Ed., P.Eng.
District School Board of Niagara

McGraw-Hill Ryerson

Toronto   Montréal   Boston   Burr Ridge, IL   Dubuque, IA   Madison, WI   New York
San Francisco   St. Louis   Bangkok   Bogotá   Caracas   Kuala Lumpur   Lisbon   London
Madrid   Mexico City   Milan   New Delhi   Santiago   Seoul   Singapore   Sydney   Taipei

**McGraw-Hill
Ryerson**

McGraw-Hill Ryerson
Principles of Mathematics 9 Student Skills Book

ISBN 0-07-097347-4

http://www.mcgrawhill.ca

2 3 4 5 6 7 8 9 0   MP   0 9 8 7 6

Printed and bound in Canada

The Geometer's Sketchpad®, Key Curriculum Press, 1150 65th Street, Emeryville, CA 94608, 1-800-995-MATH.

Statistics Canada information is used with the permission of Statistics Canada. Users are forbidden to copy the data and redisseminate them, in an original or modified form, for commercial purposes, without permission from Statistics Canada. Information on the availability of the wide range of data from Statistics Canada can be obtained from Statistics Canada's Regional Offices, its World Wide Web site at http://www.statcan.ca, and its toll-free number 1-800-263-1136.

PUBLISHER: Linda Allison
PROJECT MANAGER: Janice Dyer
DEVELOPMENTAL EDITOR: Jackie Lacoursiere
MANAGER, EDITORIAL SERVICES: Crystal Shortt
SUPERVISING EDITOR: Kristi Moreau
COPY EDITOR: Linda Jenkins, Red Pen Services
EDITORIAL ASSISTANT: Erin Hartley
MANAGER, PRODUCTION SERVICES: Yolanda Pigden
PRODUCTION COORDINATOR: Zonia Strynatka
COVER DESIGN: Pronk & Associates; Dianna Little
ELECTRONIC PAGE MAKE-UP: Jackie Lacoursiere
COVER IMAGE: Paul Rapson/Science Photo Library

Contents

Lowest Common Denominator

The lowest common denominator (LCD) is the **lowest common multiple** of the denominators of two or more fractions. You can find the LCD using multiples or prime factors.

Example: LCD of Two Fractions

Find the LCD for $\frac{1}{6}$ and $\frac{1}{8}$.

Solution

Method 1: Use Multiples

List the multiples of 6 and 8 until a common value is reached.

6, 12, 18, **24**

8, 16, **24**

The LCD for $\frac{1}{6}$ and $\frac{1}{8}$ is 24.

Method 2: Use Prime Factors

$6 = 2 \times 3$

$8 = 2 \times 2 \times 2$

The LCD will have all the prime factors of each number.

Start with the factors of the first number. Add any missing factors from the next number.

$$LCD = 2 \times 3 \times 2 \times 2$$
$$= 24$$

The LCD is 24.

Practise

1. Use multiples to find the LCD for each pair of fractions.

   a) $\frac{1}{2}, \frac{1}{3}$

   b) $\frac{1}{4}, \frac{1}{5}$

   c) $\frac{1}{3}, \frac{1}{7}$

   d) $\frac{1}{8}, \frac{1}{9}$

2. Use prime factors to find the LCD for each pair of fractions.

   a) $\frac{1}{4}, \frac{1}{8}$

   b) $\frac{1}{6}, \frac{1}{18}$

   c) $\frac{1}{8}, \frac{1}{16}$

   d) $\frac{1}{9}, \frac{1}{27}$

3. Use multiples to find the LCD for each pair of fractions.

a) $\dfrac{1}{4}, \dfrac{1}{6}$

b) $\dfrac{1}{4}, \dfrac{1}{10}$

c) $\dfrac{1}{6}, \dfrac{1}{10}$

d) $\dfrac{1}{8}, \dfrac{1}{20}$

4. Use prime factors to find the LCD for each pair of fractions.

a) $\dfrac{1}{4}, \dfrac{1}{14}$

b) $\dfrac{1}{6}, \dfrac{1}{15}$

c) $\dfrac{1}{8}, \dfrac{1}{10}$

d) $\dfrac{1}{9}, \dfrac{1}{12}$

5. Find the LCD for each set of fractions.

a) $\dfrac{1}{2}, \dfrac{1}{3}, \dfrac{1}{4}$

b) $\dfrac{1}{4}, \dfrac{1}{5}, \dfrac{1}{10}$

6. Find the LCD for each set of fractions.

a) $\dfrac{1}{3}, \dfrac{1}{4}, \dfrac{1}{6}$

b) $\dfrac{1}{2}, \dfrac{1}{5}, \dfrac{1}{15}$

7. Use the LCD to write equivalent fractions.

a) $\dfrac{5}{6}, \dfrac{2}{9}$

b) $\dfrac{3}{8}, \dfrac{5}{12}$

c) $\dfrac{1}{2}, \dfrac{3}{4}, \dfrac{1}{6}$

d) $\dfrac{2}{3}, \dfrac{1}{6}, \dfrac{7}{9}$

Add and Subtract Fractions

Fractions can be added or subtracted only if they have the same **denominator**.

For example, $\dfrac{2}{5}+\dfrac{1}{5}=\dfrac{3}{5}$

To add or subtract fractions with different denominators, the first step is to find the **lowest common denominator** (LCD).

Example 1: Add Fractions
Find each sum.

a) $\dfrac{3}{4}+\dfrac{1}{2}$

b) $\dfrac{3}{8}+\dfrac{1}{6}$

Solution

a) The LCD for $\dfrac{3}{4}$ and $\dfrac{1}{2}$ is 4.

$$\dfrac{3}{4}+\dfrac{1}{2}=\dfrac{3}{4}+\dfrac{1\times2}{2\times2}$$
$$=\dfrac{3}{4}+\dfrac{2}{4}$$
$$=\dfrac{5}{4}$$
$$=1\dfrac{1}{4}$$

b) The LCD for $\dfrac{3}{8}$ and $\dfrac{1}{6}$ is 24.

$$\dfrac{3}{8}+\dfrac{1}{6}=\dfrac{3\times3}{8\times3}+\dfrac{1\times4}{6\times4}$$
$$=\dfrac{9}{24}+\dfrac{4}{24}$$
$$=\dfrac{13}{24}$$

Example 2: Subtract Fractions
Find each difference.

a) $\dfrac{3}{4}-\dfrac{1}{3}$

b) $3\dfrac{2}{5}-2\dfrac{1}{4}$

Solution

a) The LCD of $\dfrac{3}{4}$ and $\dfrac{1}{3}$ is 12.

$$\dfrac{3}{4}-\dfrac{1}{3}=\dfrac{3\times3}{4\times3}-\dfrac{1\times4}{3\times4}$$
$$=\dfrac{9}{12}-\dfrac{4}{12}$$
$$=\dfrac{5}{12}$$

b) First, convert the mixed numbers to improper fractions. Then, use the LCD of 20, and subtract.

$$3\dfrac{2}{5}-2\dfrac{1}{4}=\dfrac{17}{5}-\dfrac{9}{4}$$
$$=\dfrac{17\times4}{5\times4}-\dfrac{9\times5}{4\times5}$$
$$=\dfrac{68}{20}-\dfrac{45}{20}$$
$$=\dfrac{23}{20}\ \text{or}\ 1\dfrac{3}{20}$$

Practise

1. Find each sum or difference. Express your answers in **lowest terms**.

   a) $\dfrac{4}{9} + \dfrac{8}{9}$

   b) $\dfrac{3}{8} + \dfrac{7}{8}$

   c) $\dfrac{3}{4} - \dfrac{1}{4}$

   d) $\dfrac{9}{10} - \dfrac{3}{10}$

2. Find each sum.

   a) $\dfrac{5}{6} + \dfrac{1}{3}$

   b) $\dfrac{3}{10} + \dfrac{2}{5}$

   c) $\dfrac{5}{12} + \dfrac{1}{6}$

3. Find each sum.

   a) $\dfrac{2}{3} + \dfrac{3}{5}$

   b) $\dfrac{5}{6} + \dfrac{3}{7}$

   c) $\dfrac{2}{9} + \dfrac{5}{12}$

4. Find each difference.

   a) $\dfrac{7}{8} - \dfrac{1}{3}$

   b) $\dfrac{8}{9} - \dfrac{1}{6}$

   c) $\dfrac{5}{6} - \dfrac{5}{8}$

5. Find each difference.

   a) $3\dfrac{2}{7} - 2\dfrac{1}{2}$

   b) $1\dfrac{5}{9} - \dfrac{3}{5}$

   c) $2\dfrac{2}{5} - 1\dfrac{1}{3}$

6. During one week, it rained for $2\dfrac{1}{2}$ h on Monday, $1\dfrac{3}{4}$ h on Tuesday, and $2\dfrac{5}{6}$ h on Wednesday.

   a) Find the total period of rainfall for this week.

   b) How much longer did rain on Wednesday than on Tuesday?

Multiply and Divide Fractions

To multiply fractions, divide the numerator and the denominator by any common factors. Any mixed numbers should first be converted to improper fractions. To divide by a fraction, multiply by its **reciprocal**.

Example 1: Multiply Fractions

Multiply.

a) $\dfrac{8}{9} \times \dfrac{3}{4}$

b) $1\dfrac{2}{3} \times 1\dfrac{1}{4}$

Solution

a) $\dfrac{8}{9} \times \dfrac{3}{4} = \dfrac{\overset{2}{\cancel{8}}}{\underset{3}{\cancel{9}}} \times \dfrac{\overset{1}{\cancel{3}}}{\underset{1}{\cancel{4}}}$

$= \dfrac{2}{3} \times \dfrac{1}{1}$

$= \dfrac{2}{3}$

b) $1\dfrac{2}{3} \times 1\dfrac{1}{4} = \dfrac{5}{3} \times \dfrac{5}{4}$

$= \dfrac{25}{12}$

$= 2\dfrac{1}{12}$

Example 2: Divide Fractions

Divide.

a) $\dfrac{2}{5} \div \dfrac{4}{9}$

b) $3\dfrac{1}{2} \div \dfrac{6}{7}$

Solution

a) $\dfrac{2}{5} \div \dfrac{4}{9} = \dfrac{\overset{1}{\cancel{2}}}{5} \times \dfrac{9}{\underset{2}{\cancel{4}}}$

$= \dfrac{1}{5} \times \dfrac{9}{2}$

$= \dfrac{9}{10}$

b) $3\dfrac{1}{2} \div \dfrac{6}{7} = \dfrac{7}{2} \div \dfrac{6}{7}$

$= \dfrac{7}{2} \times \dfrac{7}{6}$

$= \dfrac{49}{12}$

$= 4\dfrac{1}{12}$

Practise

*Express your answers in **lowest terms**.*

1. Multiply.

a) $\dfrac{3}{5} \times \dfrac{6}{7}$

b) $\dfrac{1}{3} \times \dfrac{3}{4}$

2. Multiply.

a) $\dfrac{5}{8} \times \dfrac{4}{11}$

b) $\dfrac{2}{7} \times \dfrac{3}{10}$

3. Multiply.

a) $\dfrac{1}{3} \times 2\dfrac{2}{5}$

b) $1\dfrac{1}{6} \times \dfrac{3}{7}$

c) $4\dfrac{1}{5} \times 2\dfrac{2}{3}$

d) $1\dfrac{3}{4} \times 2\dfrac{3}{14}$

4. Divide.

a) $\dfrac{4}{7} \div \dfrac{1}{2}$

b) $\dfrac{4}{9} \div \dfrac{2}{3}$

c) $\dfrac{5}{12} \div \dfrac{3}{10}$

d) $\dfrac{2}{3} \div \dfrac{7}{15}$

5. Divide.

a) $1\dfrac{1}{4} \div \dfrac{4}{5}$

b) $2\dfrac{7}{8} \div \dfrac{3}{4}$

c) $3\dfrac{1}{5} \div 2\dfrac{2}{3}$

d) $1\dfrac{2}{9} \div 7\dfrac{1}{3}$

6. A jar of jelly beans is $\dfrac{2}{3}$ full. $\dfrac{3}{8}$ of these jelly beans are orange. What fraction of the full jar are the orange jelly beans?

7. A bowl of strawberries is $\dfrac{3}{4}$ full. Janice and her friends had each eaten $\dfrac{1}{8}$ of a bowl of strawberries. How many people ate strawberries?

Add Integers

An **integer** number line can be used to add integers.

Example: Add Integers

Find each sum.

a) $5 + (-7)$ **b)** $-3 + (-4)$

Solution

a) • Start at the first integer.
   • Add the second integer by drawing an arrow.
   • The arrow points to the right if the second integer is positive, and to the left if it is negative.
   • The answer is at the tip of the arrow.

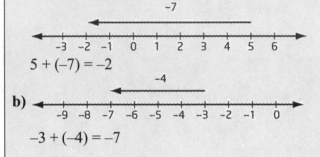

$5 + (-7) = -2$

b)

$-3 + (-4) = -7$

Practise

1. Use a number line to model each sum.

   a) $-4 + 4$

   b) $-2 + (-3)$

2. Find each sum.

   a) $3 + (-9)$

   b) $-5 + (-7)$

   c) $8 + (-8)$

   d) $-12 + 6$

3. Find each sum.

   a) $-3 + (-2) + 6$

   b) $7 + (-5) + 5$

   c) $2 + (-4) + (-3)$

   d) $-9 + 8 + (-5)$

4. The temperature in Ottawa starts at $-3°C$, rises $13°C$, and then falls $11°C$. What is the final temperature?

5. On Monday the price of a company's stock is $25 per share. On Tuesday the price drops $2, on Wednesday it rises $6, on Thursday it rises $3, and on Friday it drops $4. What was the price at the end of the week?

6. In a magic square, each row, column, and diagonal has the same sum. Find the integers that complete this magic square.

+4		
	+1	
+2		-2

Subtract Integers

Opposite integers add to zero. For example, $(+4) + (-4) = 0$.
Subtracting an integer is the same as adding the opposite.

Example: Subtract Integers
Subtract.
a) $5 - (-2)$
b) $-3 - (+1)$

Solution
a) $5 - (-2)$
$= 5 + (+2)$
$= 7$

b) $-3 - (+1)$
$= -3 + (-1)$
$= -4$

Practise

1. Subtract.
  a) $8 - 3$
  b) $5 - (-3)$
  c) $7 - 10$
  d) $1 - (-6)$

2. Subtract.
  a) $-10 - 2$
  b) $-9 - (-6)$
  c) $-1 - (-1)$
  d) $-4 - 8$

3. Fill in each ☐ with the correct integer.
  a) $5 - \boxed{} = -1$
  b) $-9 - \boxed{} = -3$
  c) $\boxed{} - (-4) = 5$
  d) $\boxed{} - 10 = -7$

4. Evaluate.
  a) $15 - 10 - 7$
  b) $4 - 12 - (-3)$
  c) $-5 - (-1) - 9$
  d) $-20 - (-5) - (-10)$

5. Which expressions have the same result?
  a) $7 - 2$
  b) $-8 - (-4)$
  c) $2 - 6$
  d) $-2 - 3$
  e) $3 - (-2)$
  f) $-9 - (-4)$

6. The average low temperature in Parry Sound in September is 8°C. In January, it is 22°C lower. What is the average low temperature in Parry Sound in January?

7. The air temperature is -10°C. With the wind blowing at a speed of 15 km/h, this temperature feels like -17°C. How many degrees does the temperature change because of the wind chill?

Multiply and Divide Integers

The product or quotient of two integers of the same sign gives a positive result. The product or quotient of two integers of opposite signs gives a negative result.

Example 1: Multiply Integers
Find each product.

a) 5×3 **b)** $-3 \times (-4)$ **c)** -5×6 **d)** $5(-2)$

Solution
a) $5 \times 3 = 15$ **b)** $-3 \times (-4) = 12$ **c)** $-5 \times 6 = -30$ **d)** $5(-2) = -10$

Example 2: Divide Integers
Find each quotient.

a) $-14 \div (-7)$ **b)** $36 \div 9$ **c)** $\dfrac{-8}{8}$ **d)** $15 \div (-5)$

Solution
a) $-14 \div (-7) = 2$ **b)** $36 \div 9 = 4$ **c)** $\dfrac{-8}{8} = -1$ **d)** $15 \div (-5) = -3$

Practise

1. Find each product.
   a) 4×6
   b) $2 \times (-9)$
   c) $(-5) \times (-7)$
   d) $(-4)(-6)$
   e) $7(-3)$

2. Find each quotient.
   a) $20 \div 5$
   b) $(-12) \div 4$
   c) $-35 \div (-7)$
   d) $\dfrac{-24}{8}$
   e) $\dfrac{-5}{-5}$

3. Multiply.
   a) $2 \times (-4) \times (-1)$
   b) $(-3) \times 2 \times 2$
   c) $(-2) \times (-3) \times (-5)$
   d) $(-6) \times 4 \times (-2)$

4. List all integers that divide evenly into each.
   a) 15

   b) -18

5. Write a multiplication expression and a division expression that would have each result.
   a) -10

   b) -12

6. Determine how each multiplication or division pattern is formed. Then, write the next two numbers.
   a) 1, 3, 9, …

   b) $-240, -120, -60, \ldots$

   c) 81, -27, 9, …

   d) 5, -20, 80, …

Distributive Property

To multiply the sum or difference of two numbers by a third number, use the distributive property.

Example: Apply the Distributive Property
Use the distributive property to evaluate.
a) 20(48) **b)** 30(32)

Solution
First, express one of the numbers as the sum or difference of two numbers. Then, apply the distributive property.

a) 20(48)
$= 20(50 - 2)$
$= 20(50) - 20(2)$
$= 1000 - 40$
$= 960$

b) 30(32)
$= 30(30 + 2)$
$= 30(30) + 30(2)$
$= 900 + 60$
$= 960$

Practise

1. Use the distributive property to evaluate.
   a) $6(80 - 1)$

   b) $0.6(10 - 0.3)$

   c) $5(100 + 20 + 9)$

   d) $4(3 + 0.9 + 0.02)$

2. Evaluate using the distributive property and mental math.
   a) 6(202)

   b) 5(87)

   c) 7(36)

   d) 3(104)

3. Evaluate using the distributive property and mental math.
   a) 2(2.4)

   b) 6(8.9)

   c) 7(3.1)

   d) 3(9.4)

4. Evaluate using the distributive property and mental math.
   a) 20(19)

   b) 30(89)

   c) 50(210)

   d) 40(320)

Order of Operations

Use the **order of operations** to evaluate expressions.

B Brackets
E Exponents
D $\Big\}$ Division and
M $\Big\}$ Multiplication, in order from left to right
A $\Big\}$ Addition and
S $\Big\}$ Subtraction, in order from left to right

Example: Apply the Order of Operations

Evaluate.

a) $2(15 - 18)$ **b)** $7 - 3(4^2 + 10)$

Solution

a) $\quad 2(15 - 18)$ **Brackets.**
$= 2(-3)$ **Multiply.**
$= -6$

b) $\quad 7 - 3(4^2 + 10)$ **Exponents.**
$= 7 - 3(16 + 10)$ **Brackets.**
$= 7 - 3(26)$ **Multiply.**
$= 7 - 78$ **Subtract.**
$= -71$

Practise

1. Evaluate.
   a) $2^3 - 4(5 + 1)^2$

   b) $3 + 2(9 - 4^2)$

   c) $-14 + 7 \times 6 - 30 \div 2$

   d) $6(3^2 + 2) - 11$

2. Evaluate.
   a) $3(-4) + (-5)^2$

   b) $4^2 \div (-12 + 10)$

   c) $-6(7 - 3) + (-3)^2$

   d) $(-1)^3 - 10 \div (-2)$

3. Evaluate.
   a) $4.1 + 0.7 \times 3 - 3$

   b) $(1^2 + 5.2) - 1.1$

   c) $(0.2)^2 + 0.5(10 - 6)$

   d) $7.3 + 2(1 + 4)^2$

4. Insert brackets to make each equation true.
   a) $15 \div 5 - 10 \times 3^2 = -27$
   b) $15 \div 5 - 10 \times 3^2 = -63$
   c) $15 \div 5 - 10 \times 3^2 = -87$

5. Fill in each $\boxed{}$ with the symbols $+$, $-$, $\times$, $\div$, and ( ) to make the equation true.
   a) $5 \boxed{} 9 \boxed{} 2 = -2$
   b) $7 \boxed{} 3 \boxed{} -4 = -5$
   c) $30 \boxed{} 12 \boxed{} -2 = -5$

Bar Graphs

A bar graph is a graph that uses bars to represent data.

Example: Read a Bar Graph

This bar graph shows the number of tickets sold during one week at the Main Street Cinema.
a) On which day were the fewest tickets sold? the most tickets sold?
b) Describe any trends in ticket sales during this week at the Main Street Cinema.

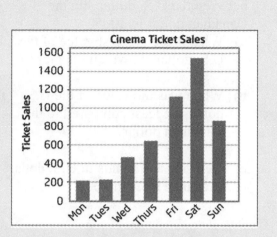

Solution

a) The graph shows that the cinema sold the fewest tickets on Monday and the most on Saturday.

b) The attendance increases from Monday to Saturday then drops on Sunday.

Practise

1. This graph shows data from a survey taken by Statistics Canada.
    a) What do the heights of the bars represent?

    b) Which provinces have an unemployment rate greater than 10%?

    c) Which provinces have an unemployment rate of about 5%?

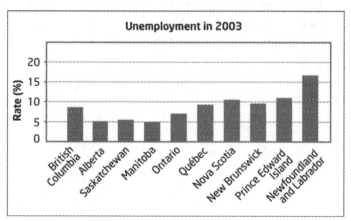

Adapted from Statistics Canada, CANSIM database, Table 109-5204, accessed via http://estat.statcan.ca, February 2006.

2. The table shows the number of members attending a fitness club during one week.
    a) Make a bar graph of the data.

Day of the Week	Number of Members
Monday	550
Tuesday	575
Wednesday	560
Thursday	580
Friday	400
Saturday	300
Sunday	200

    b) Describe any trends in member attendance during this week at the fitness club.

3. This graph shows exchange rates between the U.S. dollar and the Canadian dollar in 2005.

   a) What is the greatest value of the U.S. dollar shown on the graph?

   b) When was the value of the U.S. dollar the least compared to the Canadian dollar?

   c) Describe any trends in U.S. dollar exchange rates in 2005.

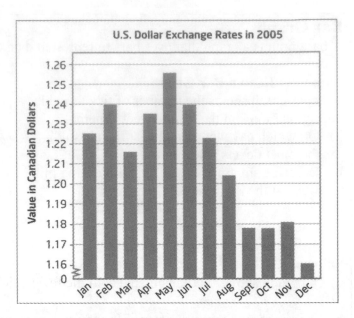

4. The table shows the average cost of 1 L of gasoline in various cities across Canada for one week in March in 2006.

   a) Make a bar graph of the data.

City	Average Cost of Gasoline (¢/L)
St John's, NL	99.7
Charlottetown, PE	92.7
Halifax, NS	99.7
Saint John, NB	99.9
Montréal, QC	95.4
Toronto, ON	88.7
Winnipeg, MB	86.5
Regina, SK	87.5
Calgary, AB	87.8
Vancouver, BC	95.4

   b) In what region was the average cost of gasoline the least? Why?

Measures of Central Tendency

The **measures of central tendency** for a set of data are the **mean**, **median**, and **mode**.

Example: Measures of Central Tendency

The heights, to the nearest centimetre, of a group of 15-year-olds are shown.

155   148   156   159   155   169   153   144   158   171   157   163

Find the mean, median, and mode.

Solution

$$\text{mean} = \frac{\text{sum of values}}{\text{number of values}}$$

$$= \frac{155+148+156+159+155+169+153+144+158+171+157+163}{12}$$

$$= \frac{1888}{12}$$

$$\doteq 157.3$$

The mean height is 157.3 cm, to the nearest tenth of a centimetre.

To find the median, arrange the values in order from least to greatest.

~~144~~   ~~148~~   ~~153~~   ~~155~~   ~~155~~   156   157   ~~158~~   ~~159~~   ~~163~~   ~~169~~   ~~171~~

The median height is 156.5 cm, or halfway between 156 cm and 157 cm.

The mode is the most common value, or 155 cm. This height occurs twice.

Practise

1. Find the mean, median, and mode for each set of data.
   a) 12, 17, 18, 17, 19

   b) 60, 65, 90, 70, 65

2. Find the mean, median, and mode for each set of data.
   a) 21, 26, 21, 26, 27, 26

   b) 85, 84, 91, 102, 87, 85

3. The masses, in kilograms, of ten different models of mountain bicycle are shown.
   15.2   14.4   12.2   16.5   13.4
   15.9   11.8   14.3   16.0   15.2
   Find the mean, median, and mode.

4. For the height data in the Example, which measure of central tendency best represents the "average" height of 15-year-olds? Explain.

5. The fuel efficiencies, in litres per 100 km, of 11 sport utility vehicles are shown.
   17.2   16.4   15.7   17.0   15.5
   16.9   17.2   15.1   13.7   16.6
   15.8
   Find the mean, median, and mode.

6. For the fuel efficiency data in question 5, which measure of central tendency best represents the "average" fuel efficiency of sport utility vehicles? Explain.

Scatter Plots

You can use a **scatter plot** to display data involving two variables.

Example: Create a Scatter Plot

The ages and annual incomes of 11 members of a family are shown.

Age (years)	25	28	32	32	33	45	47	53	54	59	60
Income ($1000)	35	75	34	37	36	44	60	51	58	68	72

Make a scatter plot of the data. Put age on the horizontal axis and income on the vertical axis.

Solution

Label the axes.

Plot the ordered pairs with age on the horizontal axis and income on the vertical axis.

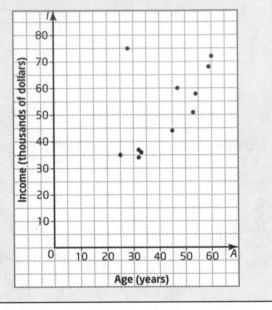

Practise

1. The table shows the wrist and neck sizes of some students.
   Make a scatter plot of the data. Put wrist size on the *x*-axis and neck size on the *y*-axis. Label the axes, and include a title for the scatter plot.

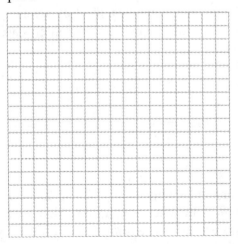

Wrist Size (cm)	Neck Size (cm)
15.5	33.0
19.0	34.5
21.5	40.5
22.5	44.0
15.0	34.0
21.0	38.9
17.0	32.0
19.5	37.0
18.0	35.0
16.5	33.5
16.0	31.0
15.0	32.5

2. The table shows approximate flight distances and times from Toronto, ON to various Canadian cities. Make a scatter plot of the data. Put distance on the *x*-axis and flight time on the *y*-axis. Label the axes, and include a title for the scatter plot.

City	Distance (km)	Flight Time (h)
Windsor, ON	315	0.7
St John's, NL	2119	2.8
London, ON	145	0.4
Halifax, NS	1289	1.8
Ottawa, ON	362	0.7
Montreal, QC	504	0.8
Timmins, ON	557	1.0
Winnipeg, MB	1503	2.3
Sudbury, ON	336	0.7
Sault Ste Marie, ON	491	0.9

3. The table shows the mean air pressure at various altitudes.
   a) Make a scatter plot of the data. Put altitude on the *x*-axis and air pressure on the *y*-axis. Label the axes, and include a title for the scatter plot.

Altitude (km)	Air Pressure (kPa)
0	101.3
2	80.0
4	62.0
6	48.0
8	36.0
10	26.0
12	19.0
14	14.0

   b) Estimate the air pressure at an altitude of 9 km.

Linear Relationships

Two variables share a linear relationship if a graph of their data forms a straight line.

Example: Graph a Linear Relationship

The table shows earnings based on time worked, in hours.

Time Worked (h)	Earnings ($)
2	20
3	30
6	60
9	90

a) Graph the relationship.
b) What are the earnings for 5 h of work?

Solution

a)

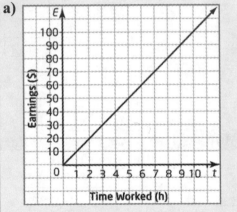

b) From the graph, earnings for 5 h of work are $50.

Practise

1. The graph shows that the relationship between the cost of apples and quantity of apples, in kilograms, is linear.

   a) Complete the table.

Apples (kg)	Cost ($)
1	
2	
3	

   b) Identify the coordinates where the graph crosses the vertical axis. Explain the meaning of this point.

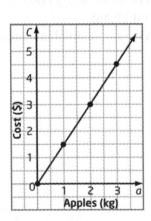

2. The graph shows that the relationship between the cost of a taxi ride and the distance, in kilometres, is linear.

   a) Complete the table.

Distance (km)	Cost ($)
1	
	3.50
4	
	5.00

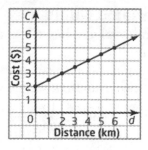

   b) Identify the coordinates where the graph crosses the vertical axis. Explain the meaning of this point.

3. Benson records the height of a tomato plant after planting it in his garden.

   a) Graph this linear relationship.

   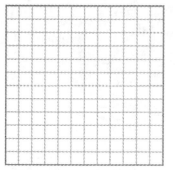

Time (weeks)	Height (cm)
1	8
2	10
3	12
6	18

   b) When does the height of the tomato plant reach 16 cm?

   c) Identify the coordinates where the graph crosses the vertical axis. Explain the meaning of this point.

4. The table shows how the distance a car travels changes with time.

   a) Graph this linear relationship.

   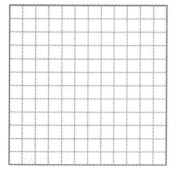

Time (h)	Distance (cm)
1	40
2	80
3	120
4	160

   b) How many hours does the car take to travel 140 km?

   c) How far does the car travel in 1.5 h?

   d) Identify the coordinates where the graph crosses the vertical axis. Explain the meaning of this point.

Rational Numbers

A rational number is a number that can be written as a quotient of two integers, where the divisor is not 0.

Rational numbers can be written in many equivalent forms.

For example, $-1\frac{1}{2}$, $-\frac{3}{2}$, $\frac{-3}{2}$, $\frac{3}{-2}$ and -1.5 are **equivalent rational numbers**.

Example 1: Equivalent Rational Numbers
Write each rational number as a quotient of two integers.

a) $2\frac{1}{3}$ **b)** 0.3 **c)** $-1\frac{1}{4}$ **d)** -1.9

Solution

a) $2\frac{1}{3}$

$= \frac{7}{3}$

b) 0.3

$= \frac{3}{10}$

c) $-1\frac{1}{4}$

$= -\frac{5}{4}$

d) -1.9

$= -1\frac{9}{10}$

$= -\frac{19}{10}$

Example 2: Order Rational Numbers
Graph the rational numbers on a number line. Then, write the numbers in order, from least to greatest.

$2.5, -3, -1\frac{1}{2}, -2.25, 0.5, \frac{5}{4}$

Solution

The rational numbers in order from least to greatest are $-3, -2.25, -1\frac{1}{2}, 0.5, \frac{5}{4}$, and 2.5.

Practise

1. In each part, decide which rational number is not equivalent to the others.

    a) $\frac{2}{5}, 0.4, \frac{-2}{5}, \frac{-2}{-5}$

    b) $-3.25, -3\frac{1}{4}, \frac{-13}{4}, \frac{13}{4}$

2. In each part, decide which rational number is not equivalent to the others.

    a) $-0.75, \frac{3}{-4}, \frac{-3}{-4}, \frac{-3}{4}$

    b) $2.2, 2\frac{1}{5}, \frac{-11}{-5}, \frac{11}{-5}$

3. Express each rational number in decimal form.

   a) $\dfrac{3}{5}$

   b) $-\dfrac{9}{10}$

   c) $\dfrac{-5}{8}$

   d) $\dfrac{13}{5}$

4. Express each rational number as a quotient of two integers.

   a) $1\dfrac{2}{3}$

   b) 0.7

   c) $-2\dfrac{5}{12}$

   d) -3.1

5. Write three equivalent rational numbers for each number.

   a) $\dfrac{7}{-8}$

   b) $\dfrac{-8}{-5}$

   c) -0.25

   d) 4.5

6. Write three equivalent rational numbers for each number.

   a) $\dfrac{-4}{10}$

   b) $\dfrac{16}{4}$

   c) $-\dfrac{6}{18}$

   d) $\dfrac{-24}{-10}$

7. Graph the rational numbers on a number line. Then, write the numbers in order, from least to greatest.

$$-2.1,\ 3,\ 1\dfrac{1}{10},\ 2.5,\ -0.5,\ -\dfrac{12}{5}$$

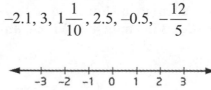

8. Graph the rational numbers on a number line. Then, write the numbers in order, from least to greatest.

$$1.5,\ \dfrac{3}{-4},\ \dfrac{-7}{-8},\ -1\dfrac{5}{8},\ -0.125,\ \dfrac{15}{12}$$

9. Fill in each ☐ with the symbols $<$, $>$, or $=$ to make the statement true.

   a) $\dfrac{3}{-8}$ ☐ $\dfrac{-3}{7}$

   b) $\dfrac{-5}{-6}$ ☐ $\dfrac{10}{13}$

   c) $-\dfrac{11}{3}$ ☐ $-3\dfrac{1}{3}$

   d) $2\dfrac{3}{5}$ ☐ $\dfrac{-13}{-5}$

10. Fill in each ☐ with the symbols $<$, $>$, or $=$ to make the statement true.

   a) $\dfrac{3}{4}$ ☐ $\dfrac{4}{5}$

   b) $\dfrac{-5}{2}$ ☐ $\dfrac{10}{-4}$

   c) $-\dfrac{1}{3}$ ☐ $\dfrac{7}{-20}$

   d) $1\dfrac{2}{7}$ ☐ $\dfrac{-13}{-5}$

Rates

A rate compares quantities that are measured in different units.

Example: Calculate a Unit Rate
A car travelled 348 km in 4 h. Write a **unit rate** that describes how fast the car was travelling.

Solution

$$\frac{348 \text{ km}}{4 \text{ h}}$$

$$= \frac{87 \text{ km}}{1 \text{ h}}$$

The car was travelling 87 km/h.

Practise

1. Calculate each unit rate.
   a) A bus travelled 288 km in 3 h.

   b) Sumi swam 50 m in 40 s.

   c) Franco ran 100 m in 20 s.

2. Calculate each unit rate.
   a) Four lemons cost $1.40.

   b) Five pairs of socks cost $12.50.

   c) Six bagels cost $7.50.

3. Calculate each unit rate.
   a) A breakfast cereal costs $3.75 for 750 g.

   b) An oatmeal raisin cookie recipe calls for 375 mL of raisins to make 30 cookies.

   c) A printer prints 45 pages in 5 min.

4. Which brand of honey is a better buy?
   Brand A: $2.44 for 250 g
   Brand B: $4.92 for 500 g

5. Which brand of maple syrup is a better buy?
   Brand A: $12.75 for 375 mL
   Brand B: $15.25 for 500 mL

6. Julie and Murray work at different coffee shops. Julie works at Starnite and earns $35 for 4 h of work. Murray works at Brew On and earns $49.50 for 6 h of work. Which coffee shop offers better pay?

Ratio and Proportion

A ratio is a comparison of quantities measured in the same units. A ratio can be written in ratio form as 3:6 or in fraction form as $\frac{3}{6}$. Similar to fractions, ratios can be written with terms that have no **common factors**, or in **simplest form**.

A proportion is a statement that two ratios are equal. For example, 3:6 = 1:2 or $\frac{3}{6} = \frac{1}{2}$.

Example: Apply Ratios and Proportions

The body of a 50-kg woman contains about 25 kg of water. The body of an 80-kg man contains about 48 kg of water.

a) Compare the mass of water in a person's body to the total mass. Write the ratio in simplest form.

b) Find the mass of water in the bodies of a 60-kg woman and a 60-kg man.

Solution

a)

Person	Ratio of Water to Mass	Ratio in Simplest Form
50-kg woman	25:50	1:2
80-kg man	48:80	3:5

b) Use a proportion.

For a 60-kg woman:

$$\frac{1}{2} = \frac{x}{60}$$

$$\frac{1}{2} \times 60 = x$$

$$30 = x$$

For a 60-kg man:

$$\frac{3}{5} = \frac{x}{60}$$

$$\frac{3}{5} \times 60 = x$$

$$36 = x$$

The body of 60-kg woman contains 30 kg of water, and the body of a 60-kg man contains 36 kg of water.

Practise

1. Write each ratio in simplest form.

    a) 6:12

    b) 15:5

    c) 16:40

    d) 100:30

2. Write each ratio in simplest form.

    a) 24:9

    b) 150:10

    c) 33:162

    d) 80:256

3. To make 1500 mL of orange juice, Tamara uses 375 mL of frozen concentrate and 1125 mL of water.
   a) Write a ratio, in simplest form, to compare the amount of frozen concentrate to the total amount of orange juice.

   b) Write a ratio, in simplest form, to compare the amount of water to the total amount of orange juice.

4. How much frozen concentrate and water are needed to make 1000 mL of the orange juice in question 3?

5. One recipe for fresh lemonade uses 425 mL of lemon juice, 2000 mL of water, and 375 mL of sugar.
   a) Write a ratio, in simplest form, to compare the amount of lemon juice to the amount of water.

   b) Write a ratio, in simplest form, to compare the amount of lemon juice to the amount of sugar.

   c) Write a ratio, in simplest form, to compare the amount of sugar to the amount of water.

6. Use the lemonade recipe in question 5.
   a) How much sugar is needed to mix with 850 mL of lemon juice?

   b) How much water is needed to mix with 150 mL of sugar?

7. Seven out of ten people prefer FastPop popcorn. How many would prefer FastPop in a group of 150 people?

8. The volleyball court is drawn to a scale of 1:300. Use the drawing to determine each of the lengths, in metres.

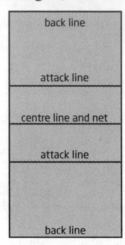

a) the length of the court

b) the distance between attack lines

c) the perimeter of the court

Percents

Percent means "out of 100" and can be written in decimal or fraction form. For example, 75% means 0.75 or $\dfrac{75}{100}$.

Example: Apply Percents

Over the track-and-field season, the height Fred cleared in the high jump increased from 1.81 m to 1.96 m.
a) Find Fred's percent increase in height.
b) What final height would Fred have to clear for a 20% increase in height over the track-and-field season?

Solution

a) Height increase = 1.96 − 1.81
                    = 0.15

$$\text{Percent increase} = \frac{\text{height increase}}{\text{original height}} \times 100\%$$

$$= \frac{0.15}{1.81} \times 100\%$$

$$\doteq 8.3\%$$

Fred increased his jump height by about 8.3%.

b) For a 20% increase, multiply by 20% or 0.2, and then add the result to the original height.
0.20 × 1.81 = 0.362
1.81 + 0.362 = 2.172

Fred would have to clear about 2.17 m to increase his jump height by 20%.

Practise

1. Express as a percent.

a) $\dfrac{1}{4}$

b) 0.245

c) $\dfrac{3}{8}$

d) 1.12

2. Express as a percent. Round to one decimal place, if necessary.

a) $\dfrac{2}{5}$

b) $\dfrac{11}{12}$

c) $\dfrac{2}{3}$

d) $\dfrac{7}{9}$

3. Write each as a decimal.

   a) 17%

   b) 33.3%

   c) 4%

   d) 105%

4. The table lists the number of days with precipitation during January in four Canadian cities. For each city, express the number of days with precipitation as a percent of the 31 days in January. Round to one decimal place.

Location	Number of Days With Precipitation
Sudbury, ON	20
Vancouver, BC	29
Charlottetown, PE	18
St. John's, NL	15

5. About 99% of the mass of the human body is made up of just six elements.
   • oxygen 65%
   • carbon 18%
   • hydrogen 10%
   • nitrogen 3%
   • calcium 1.5%
   • phosphorus 1.0%
   Find the mass of each element in a human body with mass 60 kg.

6. Jennifer's height increased from 157 cm to 163 cm in one year.
   a) Find Jennifer's increase in height as a percent. Round to one decimal place.

   b) How tall would Jennifer have to grow to have a 5% increase in height over the year? Round to the nearest centimetre.

7. A pair of designer jeans were originally priced at $129.99. The jeans are on sale for $103.99.
   a) Find the percent discount, to the nearest whole number.

   b) What sale price would represent a 25% discount?

8. A retailer buys a pair of jeans for $25, and sells the jeans for $59.99.
   a) Find the percent markup, to the nearest whole number.

   b) What selling price would represent a 150% markup?

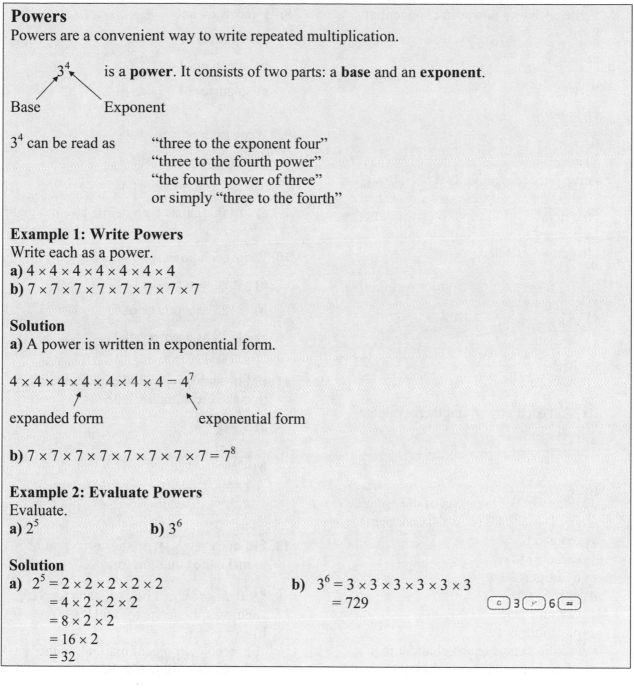

Powers

Powers are a convenient way to write repeated multiplication.

3^4 is a **power**. It consists of two parts: a **base** and an **exponent**.

Base   Exponent

3^4 can be read as   "three to the exponent four"
"three to the fourth power"
"the fourth power of three"
or simply "three to the fourth"

Example 1: Write Powers
Write each as a power.
a) $4 \times 4 \times 4 \times 4 \times 4 \times 4 \times 4$
b) $7 \times 7 \times 7 \times 7 \times 7 \times 7 \times 7 \times 7$

Solution
a) A power is written in exponential form.

$4 \times 4 \times 4 \times 4 \times 4 \times 4 \times 4 = 4^7$

expanded form   exponential form

b) $7 \times 7 \times 7 \times 7 \times 7 \times 7 \times 7 \times 7 = 7^8$

Example 2: Evaluate Powers
Evaluate.
a) 2^5 b) 3^6

Solution
a) $2^5 = 2 \times 2 \times 2 \times 2 \times 2$
$= 4 \times 2 \times 2 \times 2$
$= 8 \times 2 \times 2$
$= 16 \times 2$
$= 32$

b) $3^6 = 3 \times 3 \times 3 \times 3 \times 3 \times 3$
$= 729$

Practise
1. Write each as a power in exponential form.

   a) $5 \times 5 \times 5$

   b) $10 \times 10 \times 10 \times 10 \times 10$

   c) $8 \times 8 \times 8 \times 8 \times 8 \times 8$

   d) $12 \times 12 \times 12 \times 12 \times 12 \times 12 \times 12$

2. Write each as a power in exponential form.

   a) $1.5 \times 1.5 \times 1.5 \times 1.5$

   b) $2.3 \times 2.3 \times 2.3$

   c) $(-2) \times (-2) \times (-2)$

   d) $(-4) \times (-4) \times (-4) \times (-4) \times (-4)$

3. Write each as a power in exponential form.

   a) $x \times x$

   b) $y \times y$

   c) $r \times r$

   d) $s \times s \times s$

4. Expand each power and then evaluate.

   a) 5^2

   b) 2^6

   c) 4^4

   d) 10^3

5. Expand each power and then evaluate.

   a) 1^{11}

   b) 6^5

   c) 7^4

   d) 9^4

6. Evaluate.

   a) 1.4^3

   b) 0.5^4

   c) 0.2^5

7. Evaluate.

   a) 3.4^2

   b) 2.1^4

   c) 1.3^3

8. Express 64 as

   a) a power of 8

   b) a power of 4

   c) a power of 2

9. Write each power.

   a) 81 as a power of 3

   b) 256 as a power of 4

   c) 1 000 000 as a power of 10

10. Write each power.

   a) 4096 as a power of 8

   b) 3125 as a power of 5

   c) 1728 as a power of 12

11. Fill in each ☐ with the correct number to make the equation true.

   a) $4^6 = \boxed{}$

   b) $2^{\boxed{}} = 128$

   c) $\boxed{}^3 = 729$

12. Fill in each ☐ with the correct number to make the equation true.

   a) $11^3 = \boxed{}$

   b) $5^{\boxed{}} = 625$

   c) $\boxed{}^5 = 100\ 000$

13. The number 16 can be written as 2^4 or as 4^2. Write each of the following numbers as a power with an exponent greater than 1 in three ways.

   a) 1024

   b) 6561

Classify Triangles

Triangles can be classified using their side lengths or their angle measures.

Example 1: Classify Triangles I
Classify each triangle by its side lengths.

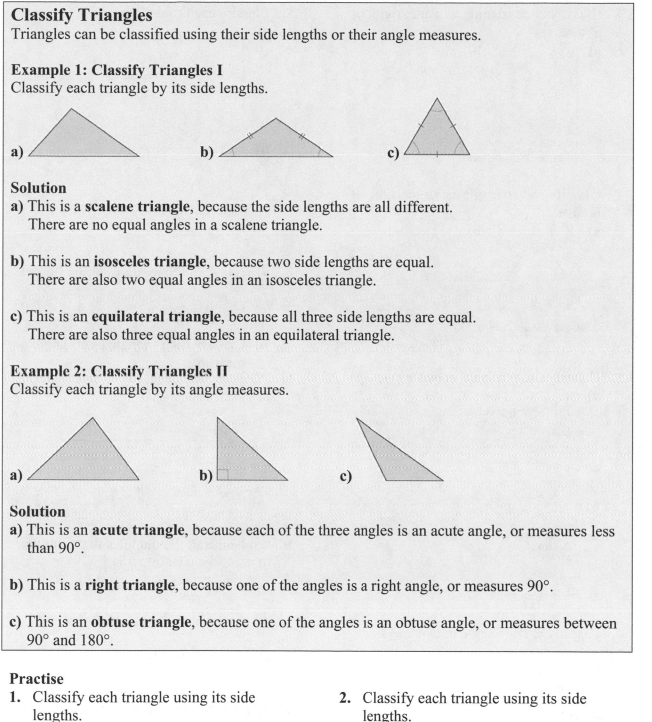

a)   b)   c)

Solution

a) This is a **scalene triangle**, because the side lengths are all different. There are no equal angles in a scalene triangle.

b) This is an **isosceles triangle**, because two side lengths are equal. There are also two equal angles in an isosceles triangle.

c) This is an **equilateral triangle**, because all three side lengths are equal. There are also three equal angles in an equilateral triangle.

Example 2: Classify Triangles II
Classify each triangle by its angle measures.

a)   b)   c)

Solution

a) This is an **acute triangle**, because each of the three angles is an acute angle, or measures less than 90°.

b) This is a **right triangle**, because one of the angles is a right angle, or measures 90°.

c) This is an **obtuse triangle**, because one of the angles is an obtuse angle, or measures between 90° and 180°.

Practise

1. Classify each triangle using its side lengths.

   a)   b)

   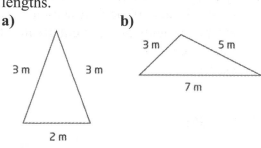

2. Classify each triangle using its side lengths.

   a)   b)

   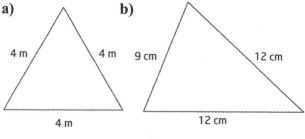

3. Classify each triangle as acute, right, or obtuse.

a)
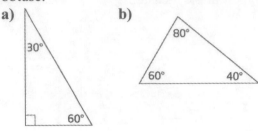

b)

4. Classify each triangle as acute, right, or obtuse.

a)
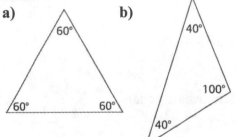

b)

5. Classify each triangle in two ways.

a)
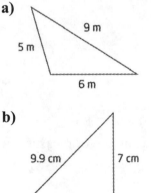

9 m
5 m
6 m

b)

9.9 cm   7 cm

7 cm

6. Classify each triangle in two ways.

a)
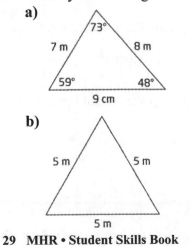

73°
7 m   8 m
59°   48°
9 cm

b)

5 m   5 m

5 m

7. Classify each triangle in two ways.

a)
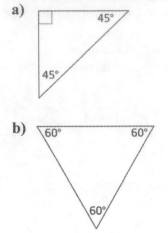

45°
45°

b)

60°   60°

60°

8. a) Name all the triangles in the figure.

b) Classify each triangle by its angle measures.

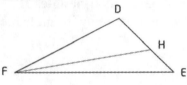

D
H
F   E

9. a) Name all the triangles in the figure.

b) Classify each triangle in two ways.

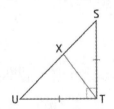

S
X
U   T

Classify Polygons

A polygon is a closed figure formed by three or more line segments.

A regular polygon has all sides equal and all angles equal.

A polygon that is not regular is called an irregular polygon.

Number of Sides	Name
3	Triangle
4	Quadrilateral
5	Pentagon
6	Hexagon

Some quadrilaterals have special names. A regular quadrilateral is a **square**. An irregular quadrilateral may be **rectangle**, a **rhombus**, a **parallelogram**, or a **trapezoid**.

Example: Classify Quadrilaterals
Classify each quadrilateral.

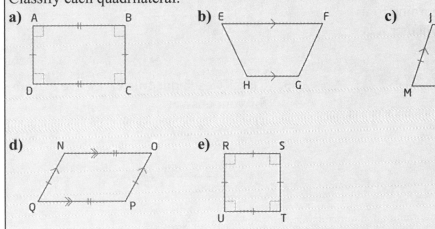

a)   b)   c)

d)   e)

Solution
a) Two pairs of opposite sides have equal lengths. All four angles are 90°.
Quadrilateral ABCD is a rectangle.

b) No sides are marked as equal. One pair of opposite sides is parallel.
Quadrilateral EFGH is a trapezoid.

c) All sides are marked as equal. Two pairs of opposite sides are parallel. The quadrilateral contains no right angles.
Quadrilateral JKLM is a rhombus.

d) Two pairs of opposite sides have equal lengths and are parallel. The quadrilateral contains no right angles.
Quadrilateral NOPQ is a parallelogram.

e) All sides are marked as equal. All four angles are 90°.
Quadrilateral RSTU is a square.

Practise

1. Classify each polygon according to its number of sides, and tell whether it is regular or irregular.

   a)

   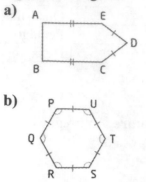

   b)

2. Classify each polygon according to its number of sides and tell whether it is regular or irregular.

   a)

   b)

   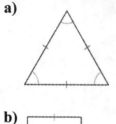

3. Classify each polygon according to its number of sides and tell whether it is regular or irregular.

   a)

   b)

   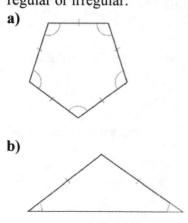

4. Classify each quadrilateral. Give reasons for your answer.

   a)

   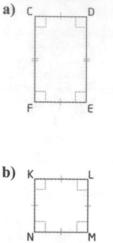

   b)

5. Classify each quadrilateral. Give reasons for your answer.

   a)

   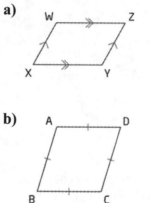

   b)

6. Name and classify the two quadrilaterals found in the figure.

   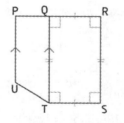

Angle Properties

You can use angle properties to find the measure of an unknown angle.

The sum of the interior angles of a triangle is 180°.

When two lines intersect, the **opposite angles** are equal.

Two angles whose sum is 180° are supplementary angles.

Two angles whose sum is 90° are complementary angles.

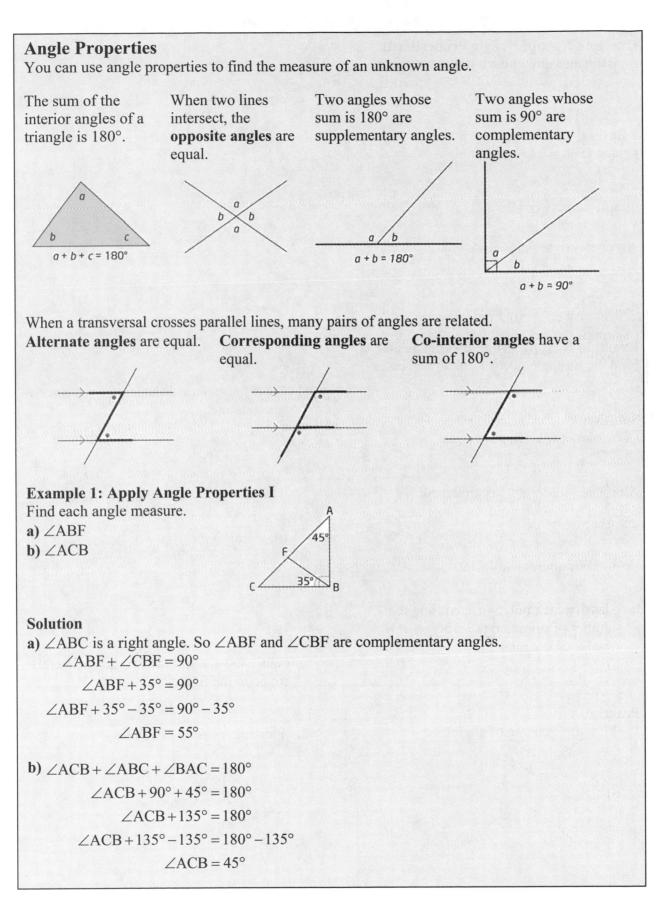

$a + b + c = 180°$

$a + b = 180°$

$a + b = 90°$

When a transversal crosses parallel lines, many pairs of angles are related.
Alternate angles are equal.   **Corresponding angles** are equal.   **Co-interior angles** have a sum of 180°.

Example 1: Apply Angle Properties I

Find each angle measure.

a) ∠ABF

b) ∠ACB

Solution

a) ∠ABC is a right angle. So ∠ABF and ∠CBF are complementary angles.

$$∠ABF + ∠CBF = 90°$$
$$∠ABF + 35° = 90°$$
$$∠ABF + 35° - 35° = 90° - 35°$$
$$∠ABF = 55°$$

b) $∠ACB + ∠ABC + ∠BAC = 180°$
$$∠ACB + 90° + 45° = 180°$$
$$∠ACB + 135° = 180°$$
$$∠ACB + 135° - 135° = 180° - 135°$$
$$∠ACB = 45°$$

Example 2: Apply Angle Properties II
Find the measure of each unknown angle.

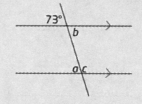

Solution
Opposite angles are equal.
$a = 40°$

Supplementary angles add to 180°.
$$b + 40° = 180°$$
$$b + 40° - 40° = 180° - 40°$$
$$b = 40°$$

Since c and b are opposite angles, $c = 140°$.

Example 3: Apply Angle Properties III
Find the measure of each unknown angle.

Solution
Corresponding angles are equal.
$a = 73°$

Alternate interior angles are equal.
$$b = a$$
$$= 73°$$

Co-interior angles add to 180°.
$$b + c = 180°$$
$$73° + c = 180°$$
$$73° + c - 73° = 180° - 73°$$
$$c = 107°$$

Practise

1. Find the measure of angle x.

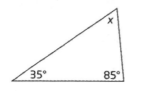

2. Find the measure of $\angle XZY$.

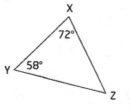

3. Find the measure of ∠PRQ.

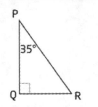

4. Find the measure of each unknown angle.

a)

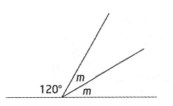

b)

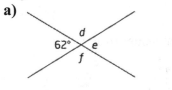

c)

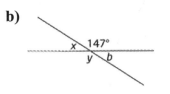

5. Find the measure of each unknown angle.

a)

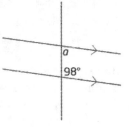

b)

6. Find the measure of angle *a*.

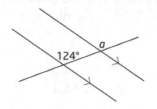

7. Find the measure of angle *b*.

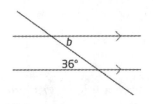

8. Find the measure of angle *c*.

9. Find the measures of the angles *a*, *b*, and *c*. Give reasons for each answer.

a)

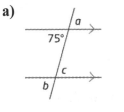

b)

Calculate Perimeter and Circumference

The perimeter of a shape is the distance around the outside.
Circumference is the perimeter of a circle.

Example 1: Calculate Perimeter
Find the perimeter of the rectangle.

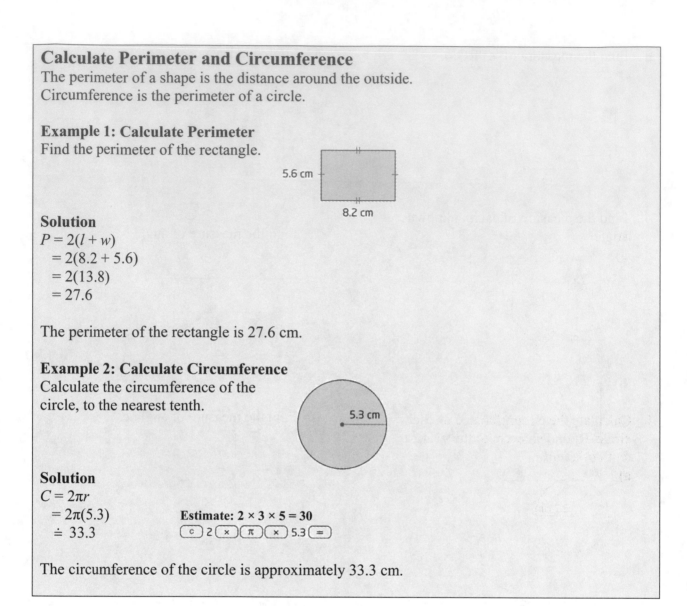

5.6 cm

8.2 cm

Solution
$P = 2(l + w)$
$= 2(8.2 + 5.6)$
$= 2(13.8)$
$= 27.6$

The perimeter of the rectangle is 27.6 cm.

Example 2: Calculate Circumference
Calculate the circumference of the
circle, to the nearest tenth.

5.3 cm

Solution
$C = 2\pi r$
$= 2\pi(5.3)$ **Estimate: 2 × 3 × 5 = 30**
$\doteq 33.3$ ⓒ 2 ⓧ π ⓧ 5.3 ⓔ

The circumference of the circle is approximately 33.3 cm.

Practise

1. Find the perimeter of each shape.
   a)

   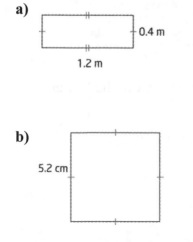

   0.4 m

   1.2 m

   b)

   5.2 cm

2. Find the perimeter of each shape.
   a)

   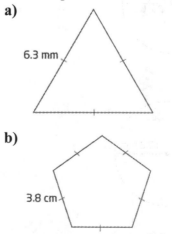

   6.3 mm

   b)

   3.8 cm

3. Find the perimeter of each shape.

a)

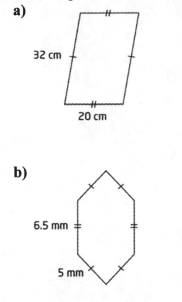

32 cm

20 cm

b)

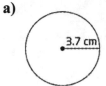

6.5 mm

5 mm

4. Calculate the circumference of each circle. Round answers to the nearest tenth of a unit.

a)

3.7 cm

b)

8.9 m

c)

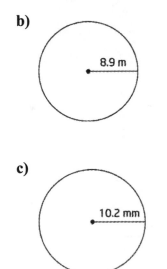

10.2 mm

5. Calculate the circumference of each circle. Round answers to the nearest tenth of a unit.

a)

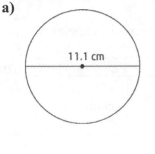

11.1 cm

b)

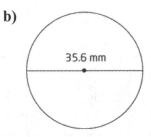

35.6 mm

c)

10.2 m

6. A flower bed has the dimensions shown.

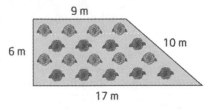

9 m

6 m

10 m

17 m

Find the perimeter of the flower bed.

Apply Area Formulas

Area measures how much space a two-dimensional shape covers. It is measured in square units.

The table gives the area formulas of some common shapes.

Shape	Name	Area Formula
	rectangle	$A = lw$
	triangle	$A = \dfrac{1}{2}bh$
	circle	$A = \pi r^2$
	parallelogram	$A = bh$
	trapezoid	$A = \dfrac{1}{2}h(a + b)$

Example: Apply Area Formula

Determine the area of the shape.

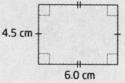

4.5 cm

6.0 cm

Solution

Use the formula for the area of a rectangle. Substitute $l = 6.0$ and $w = 4.5$.

$A = lw$

$\quad = (6.0)(4.5)$

$\quad = 27$

The area of the rectangle is 27 cm^2.

Practise

1. Determine the area of each shape.
   a)

   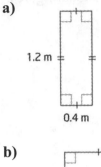

   1.2 m

   0.4 m

   b)

   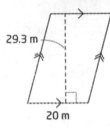

   5.2 cm

2. Determine the area of each shape.
   a)

   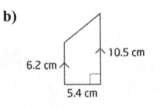

   29.3 m

   20 m

   b)

   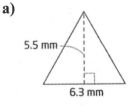

   6.2 cm   10.5 cm

   5.4 cm

3. Determine the area of each shape. Round answers to the nearest tenth of a square unit.
   a)

   5.5 mm

   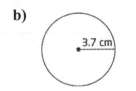

   6.3 mm

   b)

   3.7 cm

4. Determine the area of each shape. Round answers to the nearest tenth of a square unit.
   a)

   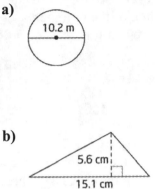

   10.2 m

   b)

   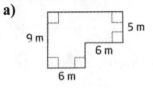

   5.6 cm

   15.1 cm

5. Determine the area of each shape.
   a)

   9 m   5 m

   6 m

   6 m

   b)

   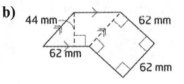

   44 mm   62 mm

   62 mm   62 mm

   62 mm

   c)

   4.5 cm

   4.7 cm

   9.4 cm

   4.1 cm

Calculate Surface Area and Volume

Surface area and **volume** are measurement concepts that apply to three-dimensional figures.

Example 1: Calculate Surface Area

Find the surface area of the cylinder, to the nearest square centimetre.

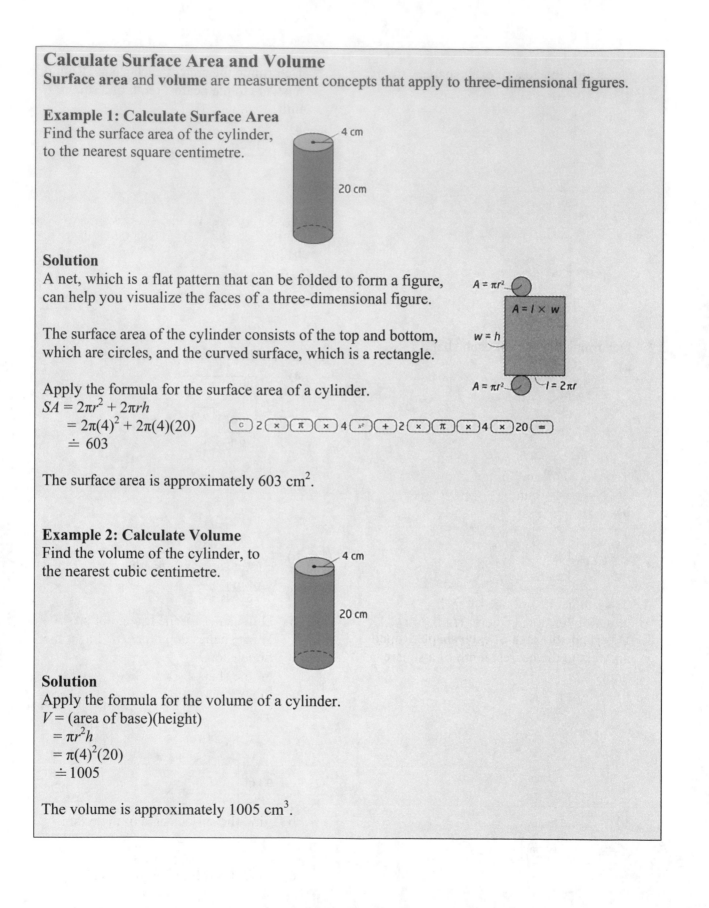

Solution

A net, which is a flat pattern that can be folded to form a figure, can help you visualize the faces of a three-dimensional figure.

The surface area of the cylinder consists of the top and bottom, which are circles, and the curved surface, which is a rectangle.

Apply the formula for the surface area of a cylinder.

$$SA = 2\pi r^2 + 2\pi rh$$
$$= 2\pi(4)^2 + 2\pi(4)(20)$$
$$\doteq 603$$

[c] 2 [×] [π] [×] 4 [x^2] [+] 2 [×] [π] [×] 4 [×] 20 [=]

The surface area is approximately 603 cm^2.

Example 2: Calculate Volume

Find the volume of the cylinder, to the nearest cubic centimetre.

Solution

Apply the formula for the volume of a cylinder.

$$V = (\text{area of base})(\text{height})$$
$$= \pi r^2 h$$
$$= \pi(4)^2(20)$$
$$\doteq 1005$$

The volume is approximately 1005 cm^3.

Practise

1. Determine the surface area of each three-dimensional figure. If necessary, round answers to the nearest square unit.

   a)

   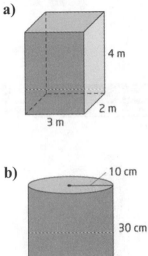

   b)

   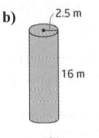

2. Determine the volume of each three-dimensional figure in question 1. If necessary, round answers to the nearest cubic unit.

   a)

   b)

3. Determine the volume of each three-dimensional figure. If necessary, round answers to the nearest cubic unit.

   a)

   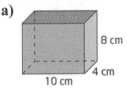

   b)

   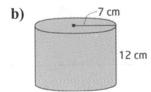

4. Determine the surface area of each three-dimensional figure in question 3. If necessary, round answers to the nearest square unit.

   a)

   b)

5. Find the surface area and volume of each three-dimensional figure. Round answers to the nearest tenth of a square unit or cubic unit.

   a)

   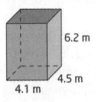

   surface area:
   volume:

   b)

   surface area:
   volume:

6. a) Draw a net for the triangular prism. What shapes do you need? Label the dimensions on the shapes in your net.

   b) Find the surface area of the prism.

   c) Find the volume of the prism.

Use *The Geometer's Sketchpad®*

The Geometer's Sketchpad® is computer software that allows the user to construct two-dimensional shapes, measures them, and transform them by moving their parts.

Example 1: Line Segment

Draw and measure a line segment using *The Geometer's Sketchpad®*.

Solution

- Use the **Straightedge Tool** to create line segment AB.
- Use the **Selection Arrow Tool** to select the line segment.
- From the **Measure** menu, choose **Length**.

Drag one of the endpoints of the line segment to change the segment's length. Notice how the measurement c screen changes as you do this.

Example 2: Triangle

Draw and measure the perimeter and area of a triangle using *The Geometer's Sketchpad®*.

Solution

- Use the **Straightedge Tool** to create three line segments to form △ABC.
- Use the **Selection Arrow Tool** to select all three vertices.
- From the **Construct** menu, choose **Triangle Interior**.
- Next, from the **Measure** menu, choose **Perimeter** and then **Area**.

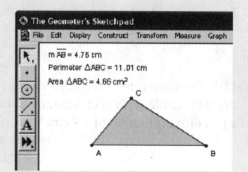

Drag one vertex of the triangle to change the triangle's shape. Notice how the perimeter and area measurements change as you drag the vertex.

Example 3: Circle

Draw and measure the circumference and area of a circle using *The Geometer's Sketchpad®*.

Solution
- Use the **Compass Tool** to create any circle.
- Make sure the circle is selected. Next, from the **Measure** menu, choose **Circumference** and then **Area**.

You can also measure the radius.
- Select the circle. From the **Measure** menu, choose **Radius**.

Change the size of the circle and watch the measurements change.

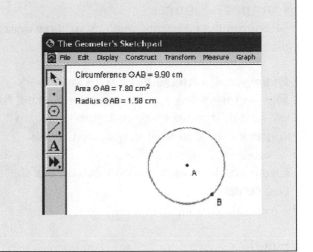

Practise
*Either draw a sketch of your results or choose **Print** from the **File** menu.*

1. Use *The Geometer's Sketchpad*® to create a triangle with each characteristic.
   a) a perimeter of 25 cm

   b) an area of 12 cm^2

2. Use *The Geometer's Sketchpad*® to create a circle with each characteristic.
   a) a circumference of 15 cm

   b) an area of 28 cm^2

3. Use *The Geometer's Sketchpad*® to create a quadrilateral with each characteristic.
   a) a perimeter of 12 cm

   b) an area of 20 cm^2

4. Use *The Geometer's Sketchpad*® to create any triangle.
   a) Measure its area.

   b) Create a circle that has approximately the same area as the triangle.

   c) Compare the perimeters of the two figures.

5. Use *The Geometer's Sketchpad*® to create any circle.
   a) Measure its circumference and area.

   b) Create a quadrilateral that has the same perimeter. Predict which figure has the greater area.

   c) Calculate the area of the quadrilateral. Was your prediction correct?

Compare Figures

Measurement concepts, such as **surface area** and **volume**, can be useful when comparing three-dimensional figures.

Example: Compare Popcorn Containers

The Pop-it-up Popcorn company is looking for the best design for an open-topped popcorn container to be used at concession stands.

Compare the volume and surface area of the two containers.

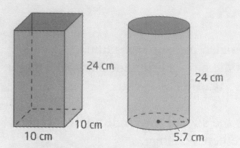

Solution

For the square-based prism:

$V = lwh$

$\quad = (10)(10)(24)$

$\quad = 2400$

$SA = A_{\text{sides}} + A_{\text{bottom}}$

$\quad = 4(10)(24) + (10)(10)$

$\quad = 960 + 100$

$\quad = 1060$

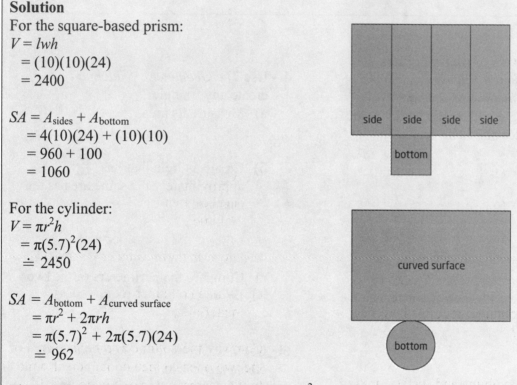

For the cylinder:

$V = \pi r^2 h$

$\quad = \pi(5.7)^2(24)$

$\quad \doteq 2450$

$SA = A_{\text{bottom}} + A_{\text{curved surface}}$

$\quad = \pi r^2 + 2\pi rh$

$\quad = \pi(5.7)^2 + 2\pi(5.7)(24)$

$\quad \doteq 962$

The rectangular prism has a volume of 2400 cm^3 and the cylinder has a volume of about 2450 cm^3, so the cylinder has a slightly larger capacity.

The rectangular prism has a surface area of 1060 cm^2 and the cylinder has a surface area of about 962 cm^2, so the cylinder requires less material to make.

Practise

1. **a)** Calculate the surface area and the volume of the two open-topped containers.

Container A

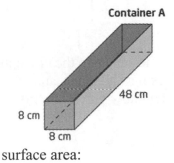

48 cm

8 cm

8 cm

surface area:

volume:

Container B

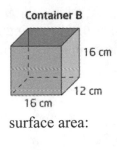

16 cm

12 cm

16 cm

surface area:

volume:

b) How do their volumes compare?

c) Which container requires less material?

2. Compare the volume and surface area of the two open-topped containers.

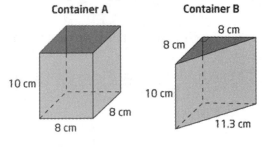

Container A

10 cm

8 cm

8 cm

Container B

8 cm

8 cm

10 cm

11.3 cm

3. **a)** Calculate the surface area and the volume of the two open-topped containers. Round to the nearest cubic or square unit.

Container A

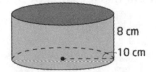

8 cm

10 cm

surface area:
volume:

Container B

32 cm

5 cm

surface area:
volume:

b) How do their volumes compare?

c) Which container requires less material?

4. Compare the volume and surface area of the two open-topped containers. Round to the nearest cubic or square unit, if necessary.

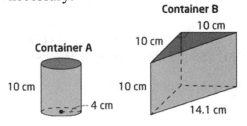

Container A

10 cm

4 cm

Container B

10 cm

10 cm

10 cm

10 cm

14.1 cm

Review of Grade 8

Measurement and Number Sense

Round your answers to one decimal place if necessary.

1. A circular field has a radius of 55 m.

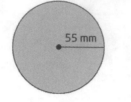

55 mm

   a) Find the circumference of the field.

   b) Find its area.

2. A disk has a diameter of 8 cm.
   a) What is its circumference?

   b) What is its area?

3. Create a concept map showing how circumference, diameter, and radius are related.

4. **a)** Construct a circle with radius 1.5 cm.

   b) Construct a circle with diameter 2.8 cm.

5. Use the diagram.

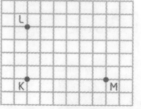

   a) Find the centre of the circle that passes through K, L, and M.
   b) Explain how you found the centre.

6. When Juliette swims across her circular pool and back, she travels a total distance of 16 m. She swims through the centre of the pool both ways. Find the surface area of the swimming pool.

7. Lars walks a distance of 120 m, halfway around a circular field. How much less would he walk if he walked straight across the diameter?

Two-Dimensional Geometry

8. **a)** Which side of △ABC is the hypotenuse?

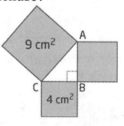

9 cm²   A

C   B
4 cm²

   b) What is the area of the square on side AB?

9. Write the following values in order from least to greatest. Label the approximate position of each value on the number line.

$\sqrt{4}$, 0.5, $\sqrt{0.64}$, $\sqrt{1}$

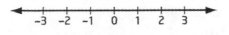

10. Estimate the length of the missing side in each triangle. Then, use a calculator to find the approximate length, to the nearest tenth.

a)

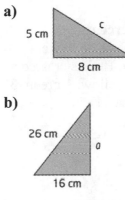

5 cm
c
8 cm

b)

26 cm
a
16 cm

11. Renata swims diagonally across a square pool. Each side of the pool is 8 m long. How many times will she need to go diagonally across the pool to complete a distance of 100 m? Round your answer to the nearest whole number.

Fraction Operations

12. Find each sum or difference. Write each answer in lowest terms.

a) $\dfrac{1}{3} + \dfrac{1}{2}$

b) $\dfrac{3}{4} - \dfrac{3}{5}$

c) $\dfrac{5}{6} + \dfrac{1}{3}$

d) $\dfrac{7}{10} - \dfrac{1}{2}$

13. One Saturday Grace spent $\dfrac{3}{4}$ h cleaning her room and $1\dfrac{1}{2}$ h cutting the grass. How long did she spend on chores that day?

14. Estimate, then evaluate.

a) $\dfrac{1}{3}$ of 20

b) $\dfrac{3}{4}$ of 30

15. On Ian's hockey team, $\dfrac{4}{5}$ of the players are right-handed. Of these players, $\dfrac{1}{2}$ have brown eyes. What fraction of Ian's team members are right-handed and have brown eyes?

16. What fraction of the rectangle is shaded?

17. Evaluate. Write each answer in lowest terms.

a) $\dfrac{5}{8} - \dfrac{1}{2} + \dfrac{3}{4}$

b) $\dfrac{1}{5} + \dfrac{5}{6} \div \dfrac{2}{3} - \dfrac{7}{10}$

18. It takes Jill $\dfrac{1}{4}$ h to type up half a page of her handwritten report. If the report is $10\dfrac{1}{2}$ pages long, how long will it take her to type up the whole report?

Probability

19. A number cube is rolled.
    a) What is the probability of rolling a 6?

    b) What is the probability of rolling an odd number?

    c) What is the probability of rolling an 8?

20. A number cube is rolled and a coin is tossed.
    a) Use an organizer to show all the possible outcomes.

    b) State each predicted probability.
    • rolling a 3 and tossing heads

    • rolling an even number and tossing tails

21. Describe an item that could be used to simulate each situation. Explain why each item is appropriate.
    a) Choose a CD from a box of 6.

    b) Choose a video to watch from a choice of 10 titles.

    c) Choose a colour of T-shirt to wear from your drawer, which contains 5 white, 3 blue, and 2 black T-shirts.

22. The weather report says there is a 60% chance of snow tomorrow. What is the probability of no snow?

23. A poll is conducted to predict the outcome of an election. Of the 200 people polled, 36 chose Brad, 112 chose Josi, and 52 chose Aaron.
    a) Based on the poll, what is the probability that Josi will win the election?

    b) What percent of the people chose Aaron?

    c) Who is the least likely to win the election? Find his or her probability of winning.

Ratios, Rates, and Percents

24. Ron is threading beads to make a friendship bracelet. He has created a pattern of 2 red, 3 yellow, 1 green, 3 yellow, and 2 red beads.

    a) What is the ratio, in lowest terms, of the number of red beads to yellow beads?

    b) Ron completes the bracelet. He uses five green beads. How many red beads does he use?

    c) There are 55 beads altogether in the finished bracelet. How many of them are yellow?

25. Selena runs 450 m in 90 s at a fairly constant speed.
    a) Express her speed as a unit rate.

    b) At this rate, how long will it take Selena to run 1 km?

26. Which is the better buy? What assumption did you make?

27. The regular price for a computer is $850. The store offers a 20% discount. The computer is subject to both PST and GST. Find
a) the amount of the discount
b) the sale price
c) the total taxes
d) the amount you have to pay the store

Patterning and Algebra

28. Josh takes mushrooms, green peppers, and tomatoes out of the refrigerator. Use Pascal's triangle to find how many different ways Josh can make a pizza with up to three toppings.

29. Examine the pattern of equivalent triangles.

inside line

a) Describe the relationship between the number of triangles and the number of inside lines.

b) Model the relationship with an equation.

c) How many inside lines are in a row of 32 triangles?

30. The value of the nth term of a sequence is $3.5 + 2n$. Write the first four terms of the sequence. Explain how you found the terms.

31. Franka is a salesperson at a health club. She earns $500 per week, plus $80 for each membership she sells.
a) Complete the table for 0 to 6 memberships sold in a week.

Number of Memberships Sold	Weekly Earnings ($)

b) Plot the ordered pairs on a grid.

c) Describe the pattern of points.

d) What will Franka earn if she sells 10 memberships in one week? Justify your method.

32. Your school holds a table tennis tournament. A player who wins a match advances to play against another winner in the next round. A player who loses a match is eliminated. How many players can enter a tournament that needs five rounds to find the overall winner?

Exponents

33. Are 2^5, 3^5, 6^5, and 10^5 all powers of 5? Explain your thinking.

34. The sum of the digits in the number 63 is a perfect square. How many other natural numbers up to 100 have this property?

35. The number of bacteria in a culture doubles every 6 h. There are 1000 bacteria in the culture at noon today. How many bacteria will be in the culture at noon in 2 days?

36. Which number is closest in value to 8.9×10^6? Explain your reasoning.
5.3×10^6
6.1×10^6
1.1×10^7
8.9×10^7

37. Estimate the height, in metres, of a stack of ten million pennies.

Three-Dimensional Geometry and Measurement

38. The front views of some objects are shown. Name two possible three-dimensional figures each might be.

a)

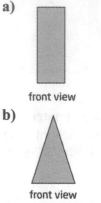

front view

b)

front view

39. Sketch the skeleton for each three-dimensional shape. How many pieces of straw would you need to build each polyhedron?
a) cube

b) square-based pyramid

c) triangular prism

40. The tent shown has an attached groundsheet. The entire outside surface is to be sprayed with waterproofing. The can of waterproofing says it will cover up to 8 m^2. How many cans are needed for this tent?

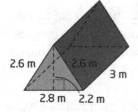

2.6 m 2.6 m 3 m
2.8 m 2.2 m

41. Gordon has a ruler that is an equilateral triangular prism. Find the volume of the ruler.

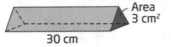

42. The dimensions of a scalene triangular prism are given.

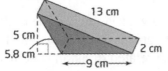

a) Determine its surface area.

b) Calculate its volume.

Data Management: Collection and Display

A sample group of teens are asked how important healthy eating is. The results for males and females are recorded separately. Use this information for questions 43 and 44.

Response	Number of Male Teens	Number of Female Teens
Very Important	14	18
Important	22	30
Not Important	4	2

43. The population for this study is 800 male teens and 1000 female teens. Use the sample data to predict how many of each gender think healthy eating is important.

44. a) Draw a comparative bar graph to show both data sets.

b) What conclusions can you draw from this graph?

45. Keira records the current temperature, in degrees Celsius, for a number of cities across Canada.

3	11	9	10
13	9	10	10
13	13	19	20
20	18	18	10

a) Organize the temperatures into intervals of 5.

b) Draw a histogram to show the data.

46. a) Describe a problem you could solve using a database in a library.

b) Describe some advantages of using a spreadsheet to create graphs and perform calculations for data.

Data Management: Analysis and Interpretation

47. Kelly is interested in being an industrial mechanic. She finds data listing starting salaries for this career. How much might she expect to earn?

Salaries ($)

Stem (thousands)	Leaf (hundreds)
30	2 3
31	1 4 4
32	8 9

48. Dominic is training for a 100-m race. His practice times, in seconds, are shown.

10.7 10.5 12.3 10.4 10.6 10.3

a) Find the mean, median, and mode.

b) One of the practice times is unusual. Recalculate the mean without this value. How much has the mean changed?

49. Claire thinks that the school's library is too small. She asks four of her friends, who all agree. She presents her findings to the student council. Identify the bias in Claire's sample.

50. Aly conducts a random survey to find which option grade 8 students prefer for a school trip. He claims that the majority of students prefer SPORTSWORLD.

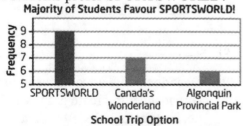

Majority of Students Favour SPORTSWORLD!

How has Aly distorted data to make a convincing argument?

Integers

51. a) Use integer chips or a number line to model $5 + (-7)$.

b) Use integer chips or a number line to model $(-2) - (-6)$.

c) Draw a triangle for the multiplication statement $5 \times (-3) = -15$. Then, write the related division statements.

52. Evaluate each expression.

a) $-2 + (-7)$

b) $-12 + 4$

c) $17 - 25$

d) $15 - (-4)$

e) -6×8

f) $-5 \times (-7)$

g) $42 \div (-7)$

h) $-32 \div (-8)$

53. Evaluate. Check your answers with a calculator.

a) $-2(5 - 9)$

b) $-6 + 3(4^2 - 6)$

c) $2^2 - 9^2$

d) $(10 - 15) \div (-5)$

54. A grade 8 science class recorded the water levels of Laurel Creek. The table shows the weekly water level readings, in centimetres, above or below the mean level.

Week	1	2	3	4	5	6
Level	−7	−9	−4	+3	−1	+6

a) The mean water level is 123 cm. Compare the 6-week mean to this value.

b) In which season might these recordings have been taken? Explain why.

55. The first four numbers in a pattern are 12, 8, 4, 0.

a) Describe the pattern.

b) Determine the next three numbers in the pattern.

Patterning and Equations

56. Model each equation. Then, solve using the opposite operation.

a) $m + 4 = 20$

b) $7 = y − 1$

c) $16 = 5x$

d) $33 = n \div 3$

57. Alfred charges $28 per month plus $9.25 per hour for cutting grass. He charges a customer $74.25 for June.

a) Model this situation with an equation.

b) How many hours did Alfred spend cutting grass in June?

58. Ruby designs patio stones using a mould of an equilateral triangle. She increases the length of each side of the triangle mould by 4 cm. The perimeter of Ruby's new mould is 90 cm. What was the original perimeter of her mould?

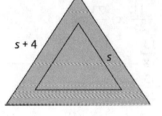

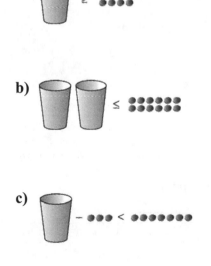

59. Model each diagram using an inequality. Then, find the whole number solution set.

a)

b)

c)

Answers

Lowest Common Denominator, pages 1 and 2
1. a) 6 **b)** 20 **c)** 21 **d)** 72
2. a) 8 **b)** 18 **c)** 16 **d)** 27
3. a) 12 **b)** 20 **c)** 30 **d)** 40
4. a) 28 **b)** 30 **c)** 40 **d)** 36
5. a) 12 **b)** 20
6. a) 12 **b)** 30
7. a) $\dfrac{15}{18}, \dfrac{4}{18}$ **b)** $\dfrac{9}{24}, \dfrac{10}{24}$

c) $\dfrac{6}{12}, \dfrac{9}{12}, \dfrac{2}{12}$ **d)** $\dfrac{12}{18}, \dfrac{3}{18}, \dfrac{14}{18}$

Add and Subtract Fractions, pages 3 and 4
1. a) $1\dfrac{1}{3}$ **b)** $1\dfrac{1}{4}$ **c)** $\dfrac{1}{2}$ **d)** $\dfrac{3}{5}$

2. a) $1\dfrac{1}{6}$ **b)** $\dfrac{7}{10}$ **c)** $\dfrac{7}{12}$

3. a) $1\dfrac{4}{15}$ **b)** $1\dfrac{11}{42}$ **c)** $\dfrac{23}{36}$

4. a) $\dfrac{13}{24}$ **b)** $\dfrac{13}{18}$ **c)** $\dfrac{5}{24}$

5. a) $\dfrac{11}{14}$ **b)** $\dfrac{43}{45}$ **c)** $1\dfrac{1}{15}$

6. a) $7\dfrac{1}{12}$ h **b)** $1\dfrac{1}{12}$ h

Multiply and Divide Fractions, pages 5 and 6
1. a) $\dfrac{18}{35}$ **b)** $\dfrac{1}{4}$

2. a) $\dfrac{5}{22}$ **b)** $\dfrac{3}{35}$

3. a) $\dfrac{4}{5}$ **b)** $\dfrac{1}{2}$ **c)** $11\dfrac{1}{5}$ **d)** $3\dfrac{7}{8}$

4. a) $1\dfrac{1}{7}$ **b)** $\dfrac{2}{3}$ **c)** $1\dfrac{7}{18}$ **d)** $1\dfrac{3}{7}$

5. a) $1\dfrac{9}{16}$ **b)** $3\dfrac{5}{6}$ **c)** $1\dfrac{1}{5}$ **d)** $\dfrac{1}{6}$

6. $\dfrac{1}{4}$

7. 6

Add Integers, page 7
1. a)

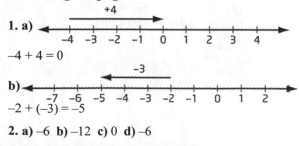

$-4 + 4 = 0$

b)

$-2 + (-3) = -5$

2. a) -6 **b)** -12 **c)** 0 **d)** -6

3. a) 1 **b)** 7 **c)** -5 **d)** -6
4. $-1°C$
5. $$28
6.

+4	−1	0
−3	+1	+5
+2	+3	−2

Subtract Integers, page 8
1. a) 5 **b)** 8 **c)** -3 **d)** 7
2. a) -12 **b)** -3 **c)** 0 **d)** -12
3. a) 6 **b)** -6 **c)** 1 **d)** 3
4. a) -2 **b)** -5 **c)** -13 **d)** -5
5. a) and e) both equal 5. b) and c) both equal -4.
d) and f) both equal -5.
6. $-14°C$
7. $-7°C$

Multiply and Divide Integers, page 9
1. a) 24 **b)** -18 **c)** 35 **d)** 24 **e)** -21
2. a) 4 **b)** -3 **c)** 5 **d)** -3 **e)** 1
3. a) 8 **b)** -12 **c)** -30 **d)** 48
4. a) $-1, 1, -3, 3, -5, 5, -15, 15$
b) $-1, 1, -2, 2, -3, 3, -6, 6, -9, 9, -18, 18$
5. Answers may vary. **a)** $2 \times (-5)$ and $20 \div (-2)$
b) -4×3 and $-36 \div 3$
6. a) $\times 3$; 27, 81 **b)** $\div 2$; $-30, -15$ **c)** $\div -3$; $-3, 1$
d) $\times -4$; $-320, 1280$

Distributive Property, page 10
1. a) 474 **b)** 5.82 **c)** 645 **d)** 15.68
2. a) 1212 **b)** 435 **c)** 252 **d)** 312
3. a) 4.8 **b)** 53.4 **c)** 21.7 **d)** 28.2
4. a) 380 **b)** 2670 **c)** 10 500 **d)** 12 800

Order of Operations, page 11
1. a) -136 **b)** -11 **c)** 13 **d)** 55
2. a) 13 **b)** -8 **c)** -15 **d)** 4
3. a) 3.2 **b)** 5.1 **c)** 2.04 **d)** 57.3
4. a) $15 \div (5 - 10) \times 3^2 = -27$
b) $(15 \div 5 - 10) \times 3^2 = -63$
c) $15 \div 5 - (10 \times 3^2) = -87$
5. a) $(5 - 9) \div 2 = -2$ **b)** $7 + (3 \times -4) = -5$
c) $30 \div (12 \div -2) = -5$

Bar Graphs, pages 12 and 13
1. a) unemployment rate for each province in 2003
b) Nova Scotia, Prince Edward Island, and
Newfoundland and Labrador **c)** Alberta,
Saskatchewan, and Manitoba
2. a) Graphs may vary. **b)** Attendance is fairly
constant from Monday through Thursday, and then
declines over the weekend
3. a) $1.255 CDN **b)** December **c)** general
downward trend from May to December

4. a) Graphs may vary. **b)** The prairie provinces, since gasoline does not have to be transported as far and taxes are lower.

Measures of Central Tendency, page 14
1. a) mean: 16.6; median: 17; mode: 17
b) mean: 70; median: 65; mode: 65
2. a) mean: 24.5; median: 26; mode: 26
b) mean: 89; median: 86; mode: 85
3. mean: 14.49 kg; median: 14.8 kg; mode: 15.2 kg
4. The mean, since the numbers are centralized.
5. mean: 16.1 L/100 km; median: 16.4 L/100 km; mode: 17.2 L/100 km
6. The median since there is an outlier.

Scatter Plots, pages 15 and 16
1. Graphs may vary.
2. Graphs may vary.
3. a) Graphs may vary. **b)** about 31.0 kPa

Linear Relationships, pages 17 and 18
1. a)

Apples (kg)	Cost ($)
1	**1.50**
2	**3.00**
3	**4.50**

b) (0, 0) This point shows the cost, $0, for 0 kg of apples.
2. a)

Distance (km)	Cost ($)
1	**2.50**
3	3.50
4	**4.00**
6	5.00

b) (0, 2) This point shows the cost, $2, for 0 km.
3. a) Graphs may vary. **b)** week 5 **c)** (0, 6) This point shows the height of the plant, 6 cm, at week 0.
4. a) Graphs may vary. **b)** 3.5 h **c)** 60 km **d)** (0, 0) This point shows the distance, 0 km, for 0 h.

Rational Numbers, pages 19 and 20
1. a) $\dfrac{-2}{5}$ **b)** $\dfrac{13}{4}$

2. a) $\dfrac{-3}{-4}$ **b)** $\dfrac{11}{-5}$

3. a) 0.6 **b)** −0.9 **c)** −0.625 **d)** 2.6
4. a) $\dfrac{5}{3}$ **b)** $\dfrac{7}{10}$ **c)** $-\dfrac{29}{12}$ **d)** $-\dfrac{31}{10}$

5. Answers may vary. **a)** $\dfrac{-7}{8}, -\dfrac{7}{8}, -0.875$

b) $\dfrac{8}{5}, 1.6, 1\dfrac{3}{5}$ **c)** $-\dfrac{1}{4}, \dfrac{-1}{4}, \dfrac{1}{-4}$ **d)** $4\dfrac{1}{2}, \dfrac{9}{2}, \dfrac{-9}{-2}$

6. Answers may vary. **a)** $\dfrac{-2}{5}, \dfrac{4}{-10}, \dfrac{2}{-5}$

b) $4, \dfrac{4}{1}, \dfrac{-16}{-4}$ **c)** $-\dfrac{1}{3}, -\dfrac{3}{9}, \dfrac{-6}{18}$ **d)** $\dfrac{24}{10}, \dfrac{12}{5}, 2\dfrac{2}{5}$

7.

$-\dfrac{12}{5}, -2.1, -0.5, 1\dfrac{1}{10}, 2.5, 3$

8.

$-1\dfrac{5}{8}, \dfrac{3}{-4}, -0.125, \dfrac{-7}{-8}, \dfrac{15}{12}, 1.5$

9. a) < **b)** > **c)** > **d)** =
10. a) < **b)** = **c)** < **d)** <

Rates, page 21
1. a) 96 km/h **b)** 1.25 m/s **c)** 5 m/s
2. a) $0.35/lemon **b)** $2.50/pair of socks
c) $1.25/bagel
3. a) $0.005/g **b)** 12.5 mL/cookie **c)** 9 pages/min
4. Brand A
5. Brand B
6. Starnite

Ratio and Proportion, pages 22 and 23
1. a) 1:2 **b)** 3:1 **c)** 2:5 **d)** 10:3
2. a) 8:3 **b)** 15:1 **c)** 11:54 **d)** 5:16
3. a) 1:4 **b)** 3:4
4. 250 mL frozen concentrate, 750 mL water
5. a) 17:80 **b)** 17:15 **c)** 3:16
6. a) 750 mL **b)** 800 mL
7. 105 people
8. a) 18 m **b)** 6 m **c)** 54 m

Percents, pages 24 and 25
1. a) 25% **b)** 24.5% **c)** 37.5% **d)** 112%
2. a) 40% **b)** 91.7% **c)** 66.7% **d)** 77.8%
3. a) 0.17 **b)** 0.333 **c)** 0.04 **d)** 1.05
4. Sudbury, ON 64.5%; Vancouver, BC 93.5%; Charlottetown, PE 58.1%; St. John's, NL 48.4%
5. oxygen 39 kg, carbon 10.8 kg, hydrogen 6 kg, nitrogen 1.8 kg, calcium 0.9 kg, phosphorus 0.6 kg
6. a) 3.8% **b)** 165 cm
7. a) 20% **b)** $97.49
8. a) 140% **b)** $62.50

Powers, pages 26 and 27
1. a) 5^3 **b)** 10^5 **c)** 8^6 **d)** 12^7
2. a) 1.5^4 **b)** 2.3^3 **c)** $(-2)^3$ **d)** $(-4)^5$
3. a) x^2 **b)** y^2 **c)** r^2 **d)** s^3
4. a) 25 **b)** 64 **c)** 256 **d)** 1000
5. a) 1 **b)** 7776 **c)** 2401 **d)** 6561
6. a) 2.744 **b)** 0.0625 **c)** 0.000 32
7. a) 11.56 **b)** 19.4481 **c)** 2.197
8. a) 8^2 **b)** 4^3 **c)** 2^6
9. a) 3^4 **b)** 4^4 **c)** 10^6
10. a) 8^4 **b)** 5^5 **c)** 12^3

8. a) 8^2 **b)** 4^3 **c)** 2^6
9. a) 3^4 **b)** 4^4 **c)** 10^6
10. a) 8^4 **b)** 5^5 **c)** 12^3
11. a) 4096 **b)** 7 **c)** 9
12. a) 1331 **b)** 4 **c)** 10
13. a) 2^{10}, 4^5, 32^2 **b)** 3^8, 9^4, 81^2

Classify Triangles, pages 28 and 29
1. a) isosceles **b)** scalene
2. a) equilateral **b)** isosceles
3. a) right **b)** acute
4 a) acute **b)** obtuse
5. a) scalene, obtuse **b)** isosceles, right
6. a) scalene, acute **b)** equilateral, acute
7. a) right, isosceles **b)** equilateral, acute
8. a) $\triangle$FDH, $\triangle$FHE, $\triangle$FDE **b)** $\triangle$FDH is obtuse;
$\triangle$FHE is obtuse; $\triangle$FDE is obtuse
9. a) $\triangle$STX, $\triangle$XTU, $\triangle$STU **b)** $\triangle$STX is obtuse and
scalene; $\triangle$XTU is acute and scalene; $\triangle$STU is right
and isosceles

Classify Polygons, pages 30 and 31
1. a) pentagon, irregular **b)** hexagon, regular
2. a) triangle, regular **b)** quadrilateral, irregular
3. a) pentagon, regular **b)** triangle, irregular
4. a) rectangle; Two pairs of opposite sides have
equal lengths, and all four angles are 90°. **b)** square;
It has four equal sides and all four angles are 90°.
5. a) parallelogram; Two pairs of opposite sides have
equal lengths and are parallel. The quadrilateral
contains no right angles. **b)** rhombus; All sides are
marked as equal. The quadrilateral has no right
angles.
6. PQTU is a trapezoid. QRST is a rectangle.

Angle Properties, pages 32–34
1. 60°
2. 50°
3. 55°
4. a) $x = 70°$, $z = 110°$ **b)** $k = 65°$ **c)** $m = 30°$
5. a) $d = f = 118°$, $e = 62°$ **b)** $x = z = 33°$, $y = 147°$
6. 124°
7. 36°
8. 82°
9. a) $a = 75°$, opposite angles; $c = 75°$, alternate
angles; $b = 75°$, corresponding angles **b)** $a = 40°$,
corresponding angles; $b = 40°$, opposite angles;
$c = 140°$, supplementary angles

Calculate Perimeter and Circumference, pages 35 and 36
1. a) 3.2 m **b)** 20.8 cm
2. a) 18.9 mm **b)** 19 cm
3. a) 104 m **b)** 33 mm
4. a) 23.2 cm **b)** 55.9 m **c)** 64.1 mm

5. a) 34.9 cm **b)** 111.8 mm **c)** 32.0 m
6. 42 m

Apply Area Formulas, pages 37 and 38
1. a) 0.48 m² **b)** 27.04 cm²
2. a) 586 m² **b)** 45.09 cm²
3. a) 17.3 mm² **b)** 43.0 cm²
4. a) 81.7 m² **b)** 42.3 cm²
5. a) 84 m² **b)** 6572 mm² **c)** 41.36 cm²

Calculate Surface Area and Volume, pages 39 and 40
1. a) 52 m² **b)** 2513 cm²
2. a) 24 m³ **b)** 9425 cm³
3. a) 320 cm³ **b)** 1847 cm³
4. a) 304 m² **b)** 836 cm²
5. a) surface area: 143.5 m²; volume: 114.4 m³
b) surface area: 290.6 m²; volume: 314.2 m³
6. a)

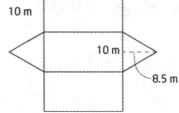

b) 685 m² **c)** 850 m³

Use *The Geometer's Sketchpad*®, pages 41 and 42
1. – 5. Answers may vary.

Compare Figures, pages 43 and 44
1. a) Container A: surface area 1280 cm², volume
3072 cm³; Container B: surface area 1088 cm²,
volume 3072 cm³ **b)** Their volumes are equal.
c) Container B
2. Container A: volume 640 cm³, surface area
384 cm²; Container B: volume 320 cm³, surface area
305 cm²; The volume of container A is twice that of
container B. Container B requires less material.
3. a) Container A: surface area 817 cm², volume
2513 cm³; Container B: surface area 1084 cm²,
volume 2513 cm³ **b)** Their volumes are equal.
c) Container A
4. Container A: volume 503 cm³, surface area 302
cm²; Container B: volume 500 cm³, surface area 391
cm²; The volume of container A is greater than
container B. Container A requires less material.

Review of Grade 8, pages 45–52
1. a) 345.6 m **b)** 9503.3 m²
2. a) 25.1 cm **b)** 50.3 cm²

3. Answers may vary.

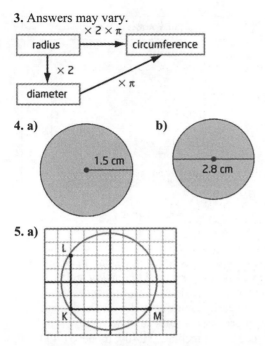

4. a) *(circle with 1.5 cm radius)* **b)** *(circle with 2.8 cm diameter)*

5. a) *(grid with circle and points L, K, M)*

b) Count the grid squares to find the bisector of KL; count the grid squares to find the bisector of KM. The point where these two bisectors meet is the centre.

6. 50.3 m^2

7. 43.6 m

8. a) AC **b)** 5 cm^2

9. 0.5, $\sqrt{0.64}$, $\sqrt{1}$, $\sqrt{4}$

(number line showing 0.5, $\sqrt{0.64}$, $\sqrt{1}$, $\sqrt{4}$ with markings 0, $\frac{1}{2}$, 1, $1\frac{1}{2}$, 2, m)

11. 9 times

12. a) $\frac{5}{6}$ **b)** $\frac{3}{20}$ **c)** $\frac{7}{6}$ **d)** $\frac{1}{5}$

13. $2\frac{1}{4}$ h

14. Estimates may vary. **a)** $6\frac{2}{3}$ **b)** $22\frac{1}{2}$

15. $\frac{2}{5}$

16. $\frac{1}{2}$

17. a) $\frac{7}{8}$ **b)** $\frac{3}{4}$

18. $5\frac{1}{4}$ h

19. a) $\frac{1}{6}$ **b)** $\frac{1}{2}$ **c)** 0

20. a)

1	2	3	4	5	6
H T	H T	H T	H T	H T	H T

b) $\frac{1}{12}$; $\frac{1}{4}$

21. Answers may vary. **a)** Use a number cube. Order the CDs from 1 to 6, roll the number cube, and choose the CD that matches the number rolled.
b) Use the ace, 1, 2, … , 9, 10 of one suit of a deck of cards. Order the videos from 1 to 10. Shuffle the 10 cards and place face down. Pick one card and choose the video that matches that number drawn.
c) Use 5 white counters, 3 blue counters, and 2 black counters. Place the coloured counters in a bag and take one out without looking.

22. $\frac{2}{5}$

23. a) $\frac{14}{25}$ **b)** 26% **c)** Brad, $\frac{9}{50}$

24. a) 2:3 **b)** 20 **c)** 30

25. a) 5 m/s **b)** 200 s

26. smaller size costs 1.475¢/mL, larger size costs 1.38¢/mL. So, the larger size is the better buy, assuming they are the same quality.

27. a) $170 **b)** $680 **c)** $102 **d)** $782

28. 8 different ways: no toppings: 1 way; one topping: 3 ways; two toppings: 3 ways; three toppings: 1 way

29. a) The number of inside lines is one less than the number of triangles. **b)** $n = t - 1$, where t is the number of triangles and n is the number of inside lines. **c)** 31

30. 5.5, 7.5, 9.5, 11.5; substitute $n = 1, 2, 3,$ and 4 into the expression $3.5 + 2n$.

31. a)

Number of Memberships Sold	Weekly Earnings ($)
0	500
1	580
2	660
3	740
4	820
5	900
6	980

b) *(graph of Weekly Earnings ($) versus Number of Memberships Sold with points (0, 500), (1, 580), (2, 660), (3, 740), (4, 820), (5, 900))*

c) For each increase of 1 horizontally, go up 80 vertically. **d)** $1300

32. 32

33. None of them are powers of 5. Powers of 5 have base 5, such as 5^3.

34. 16 (4, 9, 13, 18, 22, 27, 31, 36, 40, 45, 54, 72, 81, 88, 90, 97)

35. 256 000

36. 6.1×10^6; express all four as a number multiplied by 10^6, then compare the first numbers.

37. Answers may vary. If one penny is approximately 1.5 mm thick, then 15 000 m.

38. a) square prism, cylinder **b)** triangular pyramid, triangular prism

39. a)   **b)**

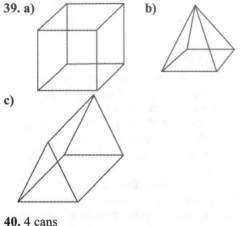

c)

40. 4 cans

41. 90 cm^3

42. a) 100.6 cm^2 **b)** 45 cm^3

43. males: 440, females: 600

44. a)

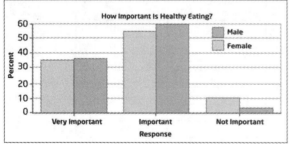

b) Answers may vary. Both males and females realize the importance of a healthy diet, but females seem to be slightly more aware.

45. a) Intervals may vary.

Temperature (°C)	Tally	Frequency
0–4			1
5–9	||	2
10–14	||||| |||	8
15–19	|||	3
20–24	||	2

b)

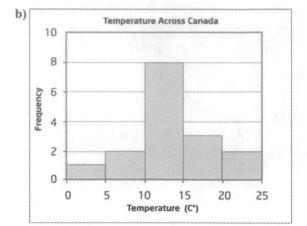

46. a) Answers may vary. You could use a library database to find books written by a particular author. **b)** A spreadsheet can be used to quickly and accurately perform calculations. Spreadsheets also quickly and easily create accurate graphs that are visually appealing and easy to understand.

47. mean: 31 443; median: 31 400; mode: 31 400. She should expect a starting salary of about $31 400.

48. a) mean: 10.8; median: 10.55; no mode **b)** The new mean is 10.5, which is 0.3 lower than the old mean.

49. Claire's sample is not random, too small, and does not represent the school population. She only interviewed her friends. Her friends are much more likely to agree with her than the average person.

50. The vertical axis starts at 5 when it should actually start at 0. The title states that a majority of students favour SPORTSWORLD, which is not true. The SPORTSWORLD bar is a different colour.

51. a)

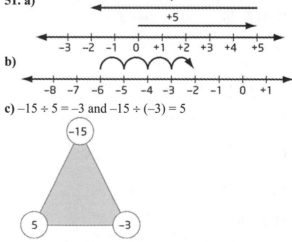

c) $-15 \div 5 = -3$ and $-15 \div (-3) = 5$

52. a) −9 **b)** −8 **c)** −8 **d)** 19 **e)** −48 **f)** 35 **g)** −6 **h)** 4

53. a) 8 **b)** 24 **c)** −77 **d)** 1

54. a) The 6-week mean is 121 cm of rain.

b) Answers may vary. The readings may have been taken during the summer because in the summer there is less than average rainfall and it is much hotter.

55. a) Each term is 4 less than the previous term.
b) −4, −8, −12

56. a) $m = 16$ **b)** $y = 8$ **c)** $x = \dfrac{16}{5}$ **d)** $n = 99$

57. a) $74.25 = 28 + 9.25t$, where t represents the number of hours worked. **b)** 5
58. 78 cm
59. a) $x \geq 8$ **b)** $2x \leq 12, x \leq 6$ **c)** $x - 3 < 7, x < 10$

Glossary

acute triangle A triangle in which each of the three interior angles measures less than 90°.

alternate angles Pairs of equal angles formed on either side of a transversal crossing a pair of parallel lines.

$b = g$
$c = f$

base (of a power) The number used as a factor for repeated multiplication.

In 6^3, the base is 6.

BEDMAS A way of remembering the order of operations. BEDMAS stands for **B**rackets, **E**xponents, **D**ivision, **M**ultiplication, **A**ddition, **S**ubtraction.

co-interior angles Pairs of supplementary angles formed between a pair of parallel lines by a transversal.

$b + c = 180°$
$f + g = 180°$

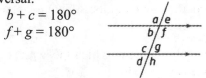

common factor A number that is a factor of (divides evenly into) all the numbers in a set.

3 is a common factor of 6, 12, and 15.

corresponding angles Pairs of equal angles, in corresponding positions, formed by a transversal crossing a pair of parallel lines.

$a = c$
$b = d$
$e = g$
$f = h$

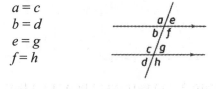

denominator The number of equal parts in the whole or the group.

$\dfrac{3}{4}$ has a denominator of 4.

equilateral triangle A triangle with all three sides equal.

equivalent rational numbers Numbers, such as $-1\dfrac{1}{2}$ and -1.5, that represent the same rational number.

exponent A raised number to denote repeated multiplication of a base.

In 3^4, the exponent is 4.

integer A number in the sequence ... , $-3, -2, -1, 0, 1, 2, 3, ...$

isosceles triangle A triangle with exactly two equal sides.

lowest common denominator (LCD) The least common multiple of the denominators of two or more fractions.

The LCD of $\dfrac{1}{2}$ and $\dfrac{2}{3}$ is 6.

lowest common multiple (LCM) The least multiple that two or more numbers have in common.

The LCM of 5 and 15 is 15.

lowest terms The form in which the numerator and the denominator of a fraction have no common factors other than 1.

$\dfrac{3}{5}$ is in lowest terms.

mean The sum of a set of values divided by the number of values in the set.

The mean of 2, 8, 4, 6, and 10 is $\dfrac{2+8+4+6+10}{5}$, or 6.

measure of central tendency A value that represents the "average" of a set of data. It can be the mean, median, or mode.

median The middle value when data are arranged in order from least to greatest. If there is an even number of pieces of data, then the median is the average of the two middle values.

The median of 1, 1, 3, 5, 6 is 3.
The median of 1, 1, 3, 5 is 2.

mode The value that occurs most frequently in a set of data.

For 1, 2, 3, 3, 8, the mode is 3.

obtuse triangle A triangle containing one obtuse angle.

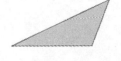

opposite angles When two lines cross, the pairs of angles formed on either side.

opposite integers Two integers, such as 5 and −5, that are equal distance either side of 0. Their sum is 0.

order of operations The convention for evaluating expressions containing several operations: Brackets, Exponents, Division, Multiplication, Addition, Subtraction. See BEDMAS.

parallelogram A quadrilateral with two pairs of opposite sides that are parallel.

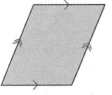

power A short form of writing repeated multiplication of the same number by itself.

5^3, x^2, and 10^7 are powers.

ratio A comparison of two quantities with the same units.

reciprocals Two numbers that have a product of 1.

3 and $\dfrac{1}{3}$ are reciprocals.

rectangle A quadrilateral with two pairs of equal opposite sides and four right angles.

rhombus A quadrilateral in which the lengths of all four sides are equal.

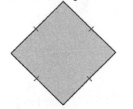

right triangle A triangle containing a 90° angle.

scalene triangle A triangle with no sides equal.

scatter plot A graph showing two-variable data as points plotted on a coordinate grid.

simplest form (of a ratio) When the terms of the ratio are whole numbers having no common factors other than 1.

square A rectangle in which the lengths of all four sides are equal.

surface area The number of square units needed to cover the surface of a three-dimensional object.

trapezoid A quadrilateral with one pair of parallel sides.

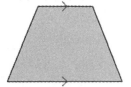

unit rate A comparison of two quantities in which the second term is 1. For example, $5 per ticket, or 30 km/h.

volume The amount of space that an object occupies, measured in cubic units.